INTRODUCTION

HOW TO HEAL A DISORGANIZED ATTACHMENT STYLE

What's happening **fearful avoidant?** Welcome - it's great to have you here.

You've basically already **completed step one - awareness.** So, **congrats on that.**

How to Heal a Disorganized Attachment Style, is here to guide you on the the next part of your journey.

You've probably **never tried a journal** quite like this before, so here's a little preview of what to expect.

Together, we'll delve into the **origins of your disorganized attachment style,** examine how your subconscious programming is **impacting your emotional responses,** practice **shadow work to heal past trauma** and learn how to **reprogram the mind** through **visualization and affirmations.**

Consider this journal your trusty companion (**we know trusting is hard for you - we'll work on it**) – a safe space to put everything you think down on paper and let go.

You might be wondering, **why shadow work?** The answer is simple.

It's a powerful psychological model that helps you **discover hidden aspects of your personality,** your 'shadow,' that often dictates your actions and reactions in ways **you might not even be fully aware of.**

We'll guide you through the journey of understanding **the role of your 'shadow,'** and harnessing this insight for **healing**.

We've created a series of prompts designed specifically for disorganized attachment to **spark introspection, understanding, and personal growth.**

Before we get started, take a moment to think about **what you aim to achieve through this journey.**

Remember that this is a safe space.

Now that you've done that, are you **ready to get started?**

Cool, **let's do this.**

UNDERSTANDING ATTACHMENT STYLES

UNDERSTANDING ATTACHMENT STYLES

Understanding Attachment Theory

First things first, let's learn a bit about **attachment theory.**

Attachment theory, at its core, is all about our **connections with others.**

It's a psychological model that attempts to describe the **dynamics of long-term relationships between humans.**

But it's not just any relationship - it's the **deep, emotional bond that forms between a child and their caregivers**, and how these early experiences of love and connection **influence us in our adult relationships.**

Biologically speaking, **humans are wired for connection**. It's not just a feel-good, optional part of life.

It's essential for survival.

In our earliest years, **forming an emotional bond with caregivers is vital** because it directly influences a **child's safety and well-being**.

The child's attachment to a caregiver is a **survival mechanism that promotes basic needs**, triggering the **caregiver's instinctual response to provide care.**

After forming these initial emotional bonds with caregivers in your early years, which are paramount for your immediate safety and well-being, the **impact of these bonds extends far beyond childhood.**

These formative experiences don't just fade away; **they embed themselves in your subconscious mind,** becoming a kind of **automatic programming** that dictates how you approach relationships and emotional situations **in adulthood.**

We'll explore this a little further later on.

UNDERSTANDING ATTACHMENT STYLES

Types of Attachment Styles

There are **4 main types of attachment styles**, each with its unique characteristics, strengths, and areas for growth. Here are the basics:

Avoidant Attachment

People with an **avoidant-dismissive attachment style** are uncomfortable with intimacy and tend to be emotionally distant. They value independence and self-reliance, often avoiding or downplaying the importance of close relationships. They may have **difficulty expressing their emotions or relying on others for support**. They often prefer to maintain distance in relationships.

Anxious Attachment

People with an **anxious attachment style** often experience a deep-seated fear of abandonment, coupled with insecurity and a desire to feel needed. This attachment style tends to emerge from experiences in early childhood where emotional needs were inconsistently met, leading to **heightened anxiety in relationships**. They may also have a **fear of rejection.** They tend to have a higher need for closeness and may experience **more frequent and intense emotions in their relationships.**

Disorganized Attachment

Also known as **fearful-avoidant,** this style is characterized by a combination of anxious and avoidant tendencies. People with a fearful-avoidant attachment style may have a **fear of both rejection and intimacy**. They may desire close relationships but also feel anxious about getting hurt or rejected. They may exhibit contradictory behaviors, such as **pushing others away while simultaneously longing for connection.**

Secure Attachment

People with a secure attachment style feel **comfortable with both intimacy and independence.** They trust their caregivers and feel secure in their relationships. As adults, they tend to have healthy and balanced relationships, with good communication, trust, and emotional support. **This is what we're aiming for!**

HOW YOU DEVELOPED A DISORGANIZED ATTACHMENT STYLE

HOW YOU DEVELOPED A DISORGANIZED ATTACHMENT STYLE

Understanding Disorganized Attachment

A disorganized attachment style is a strange combination of an **intense desire for emotional closeness**, coupled with an **intense fear of it, sending your internal alarm systems into overdrive.**

It's well...**confusing and emotionally exhausting.**

Unlike the emotional detachment associated with avoidant attachment, **your default defense mechanism involves high emotional arousal and anxiety.**

When you obsess about a relationship and the fear of being hurt, it **sends your body into "fight or flight" mode** which can **wreak havoc on the mind and body.**

The **'fight or flight'** response isn't always a bad thing.

It's actually **crucial for survival in life-threatening situations.**

Problems start to arise when 'fight or flight' **becomes a person's default setting.**

The **brain can't tell the difference** between **fearing a predator** that's about to **attack you** and fearing **something in your imagination** (i.e. remembering your ex cheating).

Both elicit the **same biological response** - all it takes is **one thought** and it's like **your mind and body are reliving that experience over and over again.**

Don't judge yourself if this sounds like you; as we mentioned this attachment style is actually **developed based on how your emotional needs were met** as a child.

You may have come from a home where you **lacked security, had inattentive** or **insensitive** parent/s or simply **lacked attention and connection.**

Maybe your parents were **trying their best** but were **too busy with work,** or **struggling with their own mental health.**

You may have also been subjected to **toxic relationships** or been **treated poorly by an ex** partner. This often leads to an obsessive compulsion when it comes to relationships.

HOW YOU DEVELOPED A DISORGANIZED ATTACHMENT STYLE

Causes of a Disorganized Attachment Style

Now let's try to identify **how you developed** your disorganized attachment style.

Chaotic Family Dynamics

Childhood Roots: Growing up in a home where unpredictability was the norm can lay the groundwork for a disorganized attachment style. Perhaps there were inconsistencies in discipline, emotional availability, or even basic care. This chaos leaves you without a stable foundation, causing confusion about what to expect from relationships.

Adult Reinforcement: You might gravitate towards unpredictable relationships that mirror the emotional landscape you navigated as a child. This perpetuates the cycle of disorganized attachment, as you shift between wanting closeness and fearing it.

Emotional Ambiguity from Parent/s

Childhood Roots: If your parent/s sent mixed signals—being nurturing one moment and dismissive the next—you probably found it challenging to develop a secure way of relating to them. This contributes to a fractured worldview where love and care are intertwined with confusion, fear, or rejection.

Adult Reinforcement: You might find that you struggle with the push-pull dynamic. One moment you crave intimacy, the next you're erecting barriers, unsure how to navigate closeness without feeling threatened.

Parental Codependency

Childhood Roots: If a parent leaned on you heavily for emotional support, the roles became reversed, putting an undue emotional burden on you. Instead of focusing on your own emotional and psychological development, you were entangled in managing your parent/s emotional well-being.

Adult Reinforcement: You might struggle with setting emotional boundaries, feeling responsible for other people's happiness or emotional stability. The pressure to be the emotional anchor for others may make it hard to focus on your own needs.

HOW YOU DEVELOPED A DISORGANIZED ATTACHMENT STYLE

Parental Alienation

Childhood Roots: Parental alienation usually occurs when one parent speaks negatively about the other, this can be during divorce, separation or even when still living under the same roof. This form of emotional manipulation can severely distort your perception of what stable relationships look like.

Adult Reinforcement: You may find yourself perpetually skeptical of partners or overly cautious in committing emotionally. Trusting someone may feel like an uphill battle, and you might subconsciously worry about choosing "the wrong side," just as you had to as a child.

Sibling Dynamics

Childhood Roots: If your relationship with your siblings was fraught with conflict, competition, or neglect, it could have impacted your attachment style. Without effective mediation from parents, sibling rivalry can escalate into a more damaging experience, leaving you with mixed feelings about trust and closeness.

Adult Reinforcement: These dynamics may play out in peer relationships or even in the workplace. You may find it difficult to establish trustful bonds or may see relationships as zero-sum games where someone has to lose for you to win.

Parental Mental Health

Childhood Roots: Having a parent struggling with mental health issues can introduce a level of inconsistency and unpredictability into your life. One day you might have experienced a warm, nurturing environment, and the next day faced withdrawal or emotional volatility from your parent. This emotional roller coaster likely left you confused about what to expect from relationships.

Adult Reinforcement: This early experience may manifest as hypersensitivity to your partner's emotional states. You may find yourself walking on eggshells, always on alert for sudden mood shifts.

HOW YOU DEVELOPED A DISORGANIZED ATTACHMENT STYLE

Parental Favoritism

Childhood Roots: Growing up feeling like the less favored child can generate a host of emotional complexities. You might have internalized the belief that you're less deserving of love or attention.

Adult Reinforcement: This early imbalance may manifest as an internal tug-of-war between wanting affection and fearing that you're not worthy of it. You might find yourself settling for less than you deserve or feeling perpetually "second best" in your relationships.

Economic Instability

Childhood Roots: Living in a household where financial security was a constant issue can result in stress and unpredictability. Whether it led to frequent moves, changing schools, or just a pervasive sense of instability.

Adult Reinforcement: You might find that you're particularly sensitive to financial ebbs and flows in your relationships, or even overly cautious or skeptical when someone offers you stability. This unease is an extension of your early experiences, sustaining the cycle of disorganized attachment as you grapple with what it means to feel secure.

Peer Bullying

Childhood Roots: Experiencing bullying, racism or social ostracization during your formative years can be particularly damaging. The experience likely led you to question your self-worth and might have made it difficult for you to form trusting relationships with your peers.

Adult Reinforcement: In your relationships today, these early experiences can resurface as a deep-seated fear of rejection or ridicule. You may find it hard to open up emotionally or to trust that you won't be hurt again. These internal conflicts can perpetuate disorganized attachment patterns, making it challenging to forge meaningful, lasting bonds.

HOW YOU DEVELOPED A DISORGANIZED ATTACHMENT STYLE

Trauma or Loss

Childhood Roots: Experiencing trauma, such as abuse, illness or the loss of a primary caregiver, can deeply embed feelings of insecurity. You might have constantly feared another traumatic event or loss, leading to anxiety about relationships and their stability.

Adult Reinforcement: Any sign of conflict or distance might be perceived as a precursor to another traumatic loss or betrayal. If an adult relationship ends traumatically, it can compound the fears originating from childhood trauma.

Busy Parent/s

Childhood Roots: Growing up with busy parent/s can create a kind of emotional vacuum. You may have been well provided for in terms of material needs, but emotional availability was often in short supply. This can create a deep-rooted anxiety, making you constantly seek approval and assurance.

Adult Reinforcement: The moment you perceive your partner as being too busy for you, it can trigger an emotional response akin to the anxiety you felt as a child. Even when you logically know that being busy is a part of adult life, the emotional imprint from your childhood can make these instances feel like impending abandonment.

Unresolved Past Relationships

Adult Origin: Even if you didn't develop a disorganized attachment style in childhood, adult relationships that were particularly tumultuous, betraying, or ended traumatically can contribute to the development of disorganized attachment tendencies.

Adult Reinforcement: Every time you enter a new relationship, past betrayals might haunt you, leading to constant anxieties about your partner's fidelity, honesty, or commitment. This isn't just a thought; it's a visceral feeling, a knot in your stomach that tightens whenever there's an ambiguous text message or an unexplained absence. These constant anxieties can become a self-fulfilling prophecy, causing you to act out or withdraw in ways that may strain the relationship, thereby reinforcing your disorganized attachment tendencies.

HOW YOU DEVELOPED A DISORGANIZED ATTACHMENT STYLE

Signs of a Disorganized Attachment Style

Now that you have some idea about how you developed your attachment style, it's valuable to have a **clear understanding of what a disorganized attachment style looks like in everyday life.**

Recognizing the signs can be the first step toward cultivating healthier relationships and greater emotional balance. Here are some of the **defining features of a disorganized attachment style:**

- **Emotional Rollercoaster in Relationships:** Your feelings toward your partner can shift quickly, from intense affection to detachment or even resentment, making it challenging to establish stable emotional ground.

- **Confusion Over Emotional Cues:** You may find it hard to interpret your partner's emotions, leading to misunderstandings and discord. Even straightforward signals could leave you puzzled, creating unnecessary tension.

- **Ambivalence About Intimacy:** Despite craving emotional closeness, you may feel uncomfortable or fearful when it's within reach. This push-pull dynamic can make both you and your partner feel unsteady in the relationship.

- **Frequent Emotional Shutdowns:** When faced with emotional discomfort, you might resort to shutting down or withdrawing, even if a part of you longs for connection and resolution.

- **Difficulty Establishing Trust:** Skepticism often lurks in the back of your mind, making it hard for you to fully trust a partner, even when they've consistently been reliable and loving.

- **Heightened Sensitivity to Conflict:** Even minor disagreements or critiques can feel like a severe threat, prompting intense emotional reactions that can be confusing to both you and your partner.

HOW YOU DEVELOPED A DISORGANIZED ATTACHMENT STYLE

- **Compulsion to Self-Sabotage:** Sometimes you might feel compelled to create chaos or disconnection in your relationships, even when things are going well, as if you're bracing for the other shoe to drop.

- **Inconsistency in Attachment Behaviors:** You might alternate between clinginess and aloofness, confusing your partner and making it difficult to establish a stable bond.

- **Preoccupation with Past Traumas:** Old wounds have a way of resurfacing in your relationships, causing you to react in ways that are disproportionate to the present moment.

- **Confusion About Self-Identity:** The emotional inconsistencies you experience can also spill into your perception of self. You may find it difficult to maintain a consistent self-image, which often leaves you questioning who you truly are, and what you genuinely want in relationships.

- **Testing the Relationship:** Your emotional ambivalence can manifest as a compulsion to "test" your partner's loyalty or love. You might intentionally create conflict or distance, just to see if your partner will stay or leave, thereby confirming your complex feelings about attachment.

- **Fear of Abandonment:** Even while struggling with emotional intimacy, a nagging fear of abandonment may linger. The paradoxical desire for closeness and the terror of being left can cause significant stress, compelling you to act in ways that might ironically push others away

By adding these **layers of understanding to your self-awareness**, you're not only getting clearer about the complexities of a disorganized attachment style but also **empowering yourself to make conscious changes.**

The knowledge equips you with the **insights needed to reshape your emotional landscape**, helping you progress toward more secure, stable, and fulfilling relationships.

HOW YOU DEVELOPED A DISORGANIZED ATTACHMENT STYLE

Triggers for a Disorganized Attachment

When you have a disorganized attachment style you may be **triggered by a number of things;** from subtle nuances in conversation, to perceiving that someone is pulling away, to reading too much into a text or feeling ignored.

Your mind is **working on overdrive trying to protect itself** from anything that might threaten your relationship. Disorganized attachment can feel triggered when:

- **Inconsistency in Communication:** A sudden increase or decrease in messages or calls from your partner can throw you off balance, leaving you to grapple with mixed emotions of wanting closeness and fearing it.

- **Ambiguity in Emotional Signals:** If your partner's emotional availability seems to fluctuate without reason, it could evoke feelings of confusion and stress, triggering you to run or sabotage.

- **High-Stress Scenarios:** Whether it's an argument or a major life change, stress can exacerbate the internal conflicts.

- **Vagueness in Relationship Goals:** If the future of your relationship is unclear, or plans are often left undecided, it can make your contrasting desires for intimacy and independence even more confusing.

- **Social Media Indifference:** When your partner is visibly active online but not engaging with you, it can trigger fears of abandonment alongside your usual apprehensions about emotional closeness.

- **Feeling Left Out:** If you're not included in your partner's plans, particularly during significant events, it can exacerbate your sense of emotional disarray.

- **Echoes of the Past:** If a current situation mirrors unresolved issues from your past or previous relationships, it can act as a trigger, activating your disorganized attachment tendencies.

HOW YOU DEVELOPED A DISORGANIZED ATTACHMENT STYLE

- **Introduction to Important Figures:** The stress of meeting important people in your partner's life can trigger fears of inadequacy, as you juggle the opposing needs for approval and emotional safety.

- **Sibling Dynamics or Parental Alienation:** Family situations that bring up historical patterns of inconsistency or neglect can be potent triggers for your disorganized attachment.

- **External Pressures:** Financial stress or work-related issues can compound your disorganized attachment triggers, making it even more challenging to navigate your emotional responses.

By understanding these triggers, you give yourself a fighting chance to **recognize when your disorganized attachment style is taking the lead.**

This **knowledge serves as a powerful tool**, enabling you to implement coping strategies that guide you toward emotional equilibrium and more fulfilling relationships.

HOW YOU DEVELOPED A DISORGANIZED ATTACHMENT STYLE

Exercise 1: Rating Your Disorganized Attachment

This exercise uses a straightforward rating system to help you **evaluate your disorganized attachment tendencies.** Rate **how true each one feels** for you on a scale of **1 (rarely true) to 10 (always true):**

- [ ] I often feel unsure about the intentions of people who are close to me.

- [ ] I have a tendency to keep people at arm's length, even if I crave closeness.

- [ ] My emotions in relationships are extremely intense, swinging from love to disdain quickly.

- [ ] I often keep my problems to myself, even from people I'm close to.

- [ ] I experience confusion about my own self-worth in relation to others.

- [ ] I often test relationships to see what their reaction is.

- [ ] Even in a committed relationship, I am prepared for it to end.

- [ ] I sometimes act out just to see if someone truly cares about me.

- [ ] I find it challenging to forgive and move on when someone has wronged me.

- [ ] I struggle with setting healthy boundaries; either they are too rigid or too lax.

- [ ] In relationships, I fear both abandonment and being smothered equally.

Low Score (1-20): Your disorganized attachment tendencies are mild. Even a minimal awareness of what triggers these tendencies can be extremely beneficial for your personal growth.

Medium Score (21-50): You exhibit moderate levels of disorganized attachment behavior. Pay special attention to the statements where you scored higher.

High Score (51+): Your tendencies toward disorganized attachment are quite strong and may require more focused effort to address.

HOW YOU DEVELOPED A DISORGANIZED ATTACHMENT STYLE

Reflection & Improvement

Now it's time to zero in on the areas where you **recognize potential for improvement.**

Turn your attention to the statements **where you rated yourself between 6 and 10** in the previous disorganized attachment exercise.

For each of these elevated scores, **consider setting a specific objective** or gaining an insight you'd like to achieve.

Example:

- If you scored high on: "**I often keep my problems to myself, even with people I'm close to**"
- Your goal could be: "I want to become **more comfortable discussing my emotions and communicating** openly with people I'm close to".

Use this exercise as **a benchmark to refer back to** as you progress through this journal.

It serves as a roadmap, ensuring the efforts you're making are in sync with the transformations you're eager to cultivate within yourself.

HOW YOU DEVELOPED A DISORGANIZED ATTACHMENT STYLE

WHAT WOULD YOU LIKE TO IMPROVE ON?

_____

_____

_____

_____

_____

_____

_____

_____

_____

_____

_____

_____

_____

_____

_____

_____

_____

_____

_____

HOW YOU DEVELOPED A DISORGANIZED ATTACHMENT STYLE

WHAT WOULD YOU LIKE TO IMPROVE ON?

_____

_____

_____

_____

_____

_____

_____

_____

_____

_____

_____

_____

_____

_____

_____

_____

_____

_____

THE POWER
OF YOUR
SUBCONSCIOUS
MIND

THE POWER OF YOUR SUBCONSCIOUS MIND

Getting Stuck in Thought Loops

Did you know, your subconscious mind is **on a constant loop?**

You've thought around **90% of the same thoughts** today as you did yesterday - this is your very own version of "auto-pilot".

It's always there, always active, **shaping the story you live every day**.

Think of it like a program that's **always running without you realizing it**.

From your subconscious mind spring your **thoughts, feelings, habits**, and ultimately, **your lived reality.**

It's really hard to **break this cycle of thought**, especially when you're not aware of it.

So, what are you thinking about?

The subconscious mind stores all of your **memories, beliefs, values, past experiences and trauma.**

If you're someone who has unresolved issues, past trauma, resentment, fear or anxiety, the likelihood is that your **subconscious narrative** or **"the voice in your head"** is mostly **fearful, negative and full of anxiety.**

For example, if you've experienced trauma that has lead to the belief that **"no one will ever want me"** your subconscious programming will continue to **reiterate and confirm that belief.**

From the moment you're born, your subconscious mind **begins to store and learn** from **every experience, every emotion, every belief,** and **all the information you encounter.**

THE POWER OF YOUR SUBCONSCIOUS MIND

Childhood Programming

We start to establish our subconscious programming between the ages of **0-7 years old.**

During this time, **both hemispheres of the brain are firing** and absorbing everything around us like a sponge.

This is where we start to become conditioned by our **families, friends, schools, religious beliefs and society.**

Through this conditioning, **we begin to develop our own personal identity** or "Ego".

By the time you reach 8 years old the **majority of your assumptions and belief systems are deeply ingrained in the subconscious mind** and will continue to **affect your behaviour into adulthood.**

So, in essence, all of your ingrained beliefs, assumptions and influences **from childhood are still triggering your subconscious mind** today **without you even realizing it.**

The mind will fight to **stay in the 'known'** - even if that means living the **same stories of pain and trauma over and over again for a lifetime.**

This is your baseline - **your mind and body's comfort zone.**

We are going to **intentionally disrupt** any negative subconscious thoughts.

By practicing **shadow work** and **understanding the mind**, we are going to **intentionally disrupt any negative subconscious thoughts** through **awareness, visualization and affirmations.**

By **intentionally changing your thought patterns** you can create **new neural connections in the brain** and **rewire your mind toward a more positive and empowering mindset.**

This is called **neuroplasticity.**

THE POWER OF YOUR SUBCONSCIOUS MIND

Rewiring Your Nervous System

When you find yourself stuck in a mental loop, **replaying the same stories and scenarios over and over again**, there's more happening beneath the surface than just a "busy mind."

These repetitive thought patterns can actually have a **physiological impact on you.**

When your thought patterns are largely **negative, fear-based, or anchored in past traumas** it can lead to a **disregulated nervous system.**

What does that mean?

Well, it **throws your stress response mechanisms out of whack**, making it **more challenging to cope with day-to-day pressures.**

Your body can't differentiate between **a vivid thought or memory and an actual experience;** both trigger the **same physiological responses.**

These incessant loops **contribute to your body's production of stress hormones like cortisol and adrenaline**, setting off a domino effect that can influence everything from **your mood to your immune system.**

This cycle of biochemical responses can perpetuate your state of being, **keeping you locked in a reactive mode rather than a proactive one.**

The **subconscious mind clings to the stories you tell yourself,** the **memories you sit with** and continues to **send the same thoughts to you over and over again.**

So, breaking free from these repetitive thought loops isn't just about achieving mental clarity; it's about **recalibrating an entire system — your mind-body network —** to function in a way that **supports your holistic well-being.**

It's cool though, **we're going to work on this together.**

24

THE POWER OF YOUR SUBCONSCIOUS MIND

Awareness & Listening to Your Thoughts

Now that you have an awareness of your subconscious loop, **it's time to disrupt it.**

Your internal dialogue is geared towards **making sure you're loved and valued, but it has a way of creating emotional turbulence.**

This often manifests as **heightened sensitivity to your partner's moods, words, and actions**—always scanning for **signs of approval or disapproval.**

Your subconscious **feeds you lines** that you need constant reassurance to feel secure, which just **fuels your cycle of emotional neediness.**

Remember, the **body doesn't know the difference between a thought and a real experience.**

Every time you think **about that fight from a few weeks ago,** or a **bad childhood memory,** or that **ex that cheated on you,** your brain thinks it's happening **right now.**

Can you see how that's a problem? Your **internal alarms are always activated** and we need to **start working on that.**

Here's the truth: **it's you vs you here.**

You're **challenging your default programming** by interrupting it and sending it new messaging.

You're taking control by understanding that **<u>you are not your thoughts</u>** - crazy, right?

The more you pay attention to what's going on in your brain, the more you can actively **choose your thoughts.**

When your brain starts to hear **positive thoughts** as opposed to **negative or fearful thoughts**, it **starts to believe them.**

It's like giving yourself a software update - that loop that you've been stuck in for **months, years or even decades** starts to shift and change. **Make sense?**

It takes **30 days to create new neural pathways**.

Are you ready to start **rewiring the mind together?**

THE POWER OF YOUR SUBCONSCIOUS MIND

Techniques for Listening to Your Thoughts

Let's **take back control** of your mind, shall we? Make a commitment out loud to yourself right now, say: **"I am going to start listening to my thoughts"** - this is setting a reminder for your brain.

Now let's **start practicing.**

Technique 1: Catching & Challenging

The first technique is **catching and challenging your thoughts.** What's something that consistently pops up in your mind that is **causing you stress or anxiety at the moment? Write it down.**

_____

_____

_____

We're going to use this situation **as a test.**

For the next few weeks, every time you think about this situation, try to **catch the thought.**

It sounds **a little weird,** but now that you have an **awareness** of your loop you're going to see that your **brain runs off on tangents all the time** without you even consciously realizing it.

Once you catch the thought **"observe it".**

Challenge it.
- Was it valid? Do you agree?
- Why are you thinking it?
- Where did the thought come from?
- Has this thought been on loop for more than one day?
- What can you do about the thought?

Interrupt the thought - literally - **tell yourself to stop** - **shift your focus to something else** and continue to do this **as often as possible when you catch the thought.**

THE POWER OF YOUR SUBCONSCIOUS MIND

Technique 2: Breathwork

If you ever find yourself in a **mental spiral** or feeling **particularly stressed**, you can use **breathwork to redirect your thoughts**.

Why breathwork?

When you take **slow, deep breaths**, you're sending **signals to your brain to chill out.**

Deep breathing activates the **vagus nerve**, the largest nerve in the body, that connects the brainstem to all of your major organs and **is responsible for regulating emotion.**

Stimulating this nerve **kicks your parasympathetic nervous system** into gear—that's the **"rest and digest"** part of your autonomic nervous system.

This **counters the stress-induced "fight or flight"** mode, **dialing down the production of stress hormones like cortisol.**

What you get is a **calmer mind**, **lower heart rate**, and a **sense of equilibrium**, making it easier to **tackle any thoughts or challenges that come your way.**

So, the next time you breathe deeply, know that you're doing some **instant neuroscience to get your system back on track.**

Tips for Breathwork

- Try to **focus your mind on the air entering your nose** and **exiting your mouth.**
- When you catch yourself thinking again, **redirect your mind to the breath.**
- Make your first breath **slow and deep.**

Here's one simple technique that helps you regulate your nervous system:

- 1 deep inhale through the nose, fill your belly, followed by;
- 1 short inhale through the nose, up to your chest, then;
- Hold at the top of your head for 8-10 seconds, followed by;
- 1 long exhale for 6-8 seconds through the mouth,
- Repeat 3-10 times.

THE POWER OF YOUR SUBCONSCIOUS MIND

Technique 3: You vs Your Phone

When you wake up in the morning, **what's the first thing that you do?**

Grab your phone? **Thought so.**

When you wake up, your brain is transitioning from a **theta state**—a deeply relaxed, borderline meditative state—to a more alert alpha or beta state.

This is a crucial time for **setting intentions and framing your mindset for the day.**

Reaching for your phone **disrupts this process.**

It **immediately puts you in a reactive mode**, absorbing external stimuli like **emails, social media, and news.**

This can cause a **spike in stress hormones** and conditions your brain to be more reactive and less intentional throughout the day.

In essence, you're forfeiting your first moments of the day to external circumstances, instead of **consciously steering them to align with your own well-being and goals.**

We know that this one is going to be hard **but you're here to make changes**, right? And you're probably going to fail some days, **but that's okay, try again the next day.**

Here's what to do on **days that you do remember:**

- Realize that you're waking up - oh hey.
- Consciously stop yourself from touching your phone.
- Stay in your bed and lay on your back
- Take 10-20 deep breaths, **inhaling through the mouth** and **exhaling through the mouth**
- Take a moment to lay in a calm state after your breaths
- Tell yourself that you're going to own the day in whatever words feel authentic to you.

Then when you're done - grab your phone - **we know you want to.**

This is a really interesting **you vs you moment. Your mind and body will fight you on this.**

The question is - **who will win?**

THE POWER OF YOUR SUBCONSCIOUS MIND

Technique 4: Mirror Talk

This one's pretty simple but something **you've probably never done.**

Mirror talk.

Every time you catch yourself in the mirror look into your eyes and say a positive mantra to yourself; **something like "damn I am f***ing sexy" or "I am feeling incredible today" or "I am crushing it today".**

Use words that **resonate with you** but make sure they are **positive** and use an **"I am"** statement.

Even on days you don't believe it, **make it a habit.**

Make it short - **make an impact with it.**

Write down your mantra:

_____

_____

Say it out loud when you're alone and **in your head** when people are around (we don't want them to think you're crazy).

Try to do this as often as possible - it'll start to **become a habit and you'll find yourself automatically saying it at some point.**

You might even start to really **believe it.**

THE POWER OF YOUR SUBCONSCIOUS MIND

Exercise 2: Your Web of Beliefs

We've talked a lot about your attachment style and how your subconscious programming is shaping your life and we'll continue to unpack that more later, aside from that - **who are you as of right now?**

What do <u>you</u> believe?

We're now going to do an exercise to **map out your web of beliefs.**

1. On the next page draw lines radiating out from "My Beliefs", like a web.

2. At the end of each line, write a **belief or assumption** you hold about yourself, others, or the world. For example what do you believe about:
    - Life - is it fair?
    - Love - do you believe in it?
    - People's opinion's about you?
    - How you look?
    - Where you are in life?
    - Failure
    - Expectations
    - Your ability to change your life
    - The purpose of life?
    - What the future holds?

3. Once you've filled the page, take a step back. Look at your Belief Web. **Are there any beliefs that surprise you? Any patterns?** Any beliefs that might be **holding you back from fully accepting yourself?**

4. Circle the beliefs **you want to work on** changing throughout your journey.

THE POWER OF YOUR SUBCONSCIOUS MIND

My Beliefs

THE LAW
OF DETACHMENT

THE LAW OF DETACHMENT

Law of Detachment Basics

Hopefully at this point you've learnt some **really cool stuff about how your brain works.**

Now let's talk about the **law of detachment and how it can help.**

The law of detachment is the simple understanding that **we are not in control of other people's actions.**

It's the idea that in order to manifest our desires that we have to **release ourselves from the attachment to an outcome.**

When you let go in this manner, **you no longer feel the compulsion to obsess** over every detail when it comes to love and relationships.

This can be particularly difficult for someone with a **disorganized attachment style.**

Sometimes the desire to control is so strong that it is **mentally overwhelming.**

By letting go of our **obsessive focus on specific outcomes**, by releasing the need to control every detail, we free ourselves from the constraints of "lack" thinking.

Let's get into the fundamental principles of the **law of detachment.**

THE LAW OF DETACHMENT

Presence

Presence is a fundamental aspect of the law of detachment - sounds simple, **but being present can actually be really difficult.**

It involves living in the present moment and **not being stuck in your head with all that chatter all the time.**

When you direct your attention to **what's happening at this very moment,** you create mental space.

This mental freedom **lets you evaluate your thoughts, your choices, and yes, even your relationships,** from a fresher perspective.

So, **how do you do this?**

You're **already starting to practice catching your negative thoughts,** but this is a little different.

Begin by **catching yourself when you start drifting away in any thought.**

Acknowledge it without judgment and guide your **focus back to the now - on whatever you're doing.**

This isn't a one-time fix; **it's a practice.**

You don't need to do this all the time but **having this awareness can really help to clear your mind** and **stop overthinking.**

A fun little trick to try and quiet the mind is to ask yourself **"I wonder what thought I'll think of next".**

Do this the next time you find yourself distracted - **you might be surprised at what your brain does.**

THE LAW OF DETACHMENT

Acceptance

There's a reason why the saying goes "**expectation is the thief of joy**".

Simply don't have any.

When you have a **rigid idea in your head** about how someone should behave, **you're setting yourself up for failure.**

Obsessing over someone else's behaviour **doesn't change them** - it just stresses you out.

When you focus inwardly and **detach from expectations** you gain more clarity on what you deserve and whether the person you're interested in can provide that.

Sometimes, they are capable and **other times it's time to move on** (we know this seems impossible and is really difficult to accept - but you can do it!)

You simply can't force someone to be who you want them to be - **it has to ultimately be their decision**.

Detaching from this expectation will allow you the space to **understand your emotions and what's right for you.**

Spend your time and energy on becoming a **better you**.

Do things that **make you feel happy and confident** - prioritize your **personal growth** and healing.

When your whole world **revolves around the love of another person** you are constantly signalling lack, worry, disappointment to the mind - **which encourages anxious and negative thoughts.**

When you **focus on things that make you feel happy** you are attracting **more happiness.**

Put yourself out there, do something **fun and creative that keeps you present**, try **new things** and **distract the mind from compulsive thoughts.**

THE LAW OF DETACHMENT

Letting Go

Letting go is a crucial aspect of the law of detachment.

It involves **releasing attachment to what no longer serves your growth** and happiness.

It's not about being indifferent or uncaring but rather making room for new experiences and opportunities that **align more authentically with your current self.**

Letting go is an act of **trust** that allows you to **move forward with freedom and openness.**

- Release attachment to **past hurts, resentments, and disappointments.**
- Let go of relationships that are **no longer healthy or fulfilling.**
- Detach from the **need for external validation** and approval.
- **Surrender control over the outcomes** and trust in the natural flow of life.
- Make space for **new experiences, growth, and opportunities.**

These fundamentals of the law of detachment empower you to **live authentically, embrace uncertainty, and allow the natural unfolding** of your journey.

Don't worry if this all seems too difficult, we'll help you work through these emotions in the **shadow work prompt section.**

Tips for Letting Go

1. Allow others to **be who they are**
2. Allow yourself to **be who you are**
3. Don't **force** situations
4. Solutions will emerge **when you least expect them**
5. **Uncertainty is a reality**
6. Obsessing over something **doesn't change it**
7. Obsessing over someone **doesn't change them**
8. **Embrace it**
9. **Let go**

THE LAW OF DETACHMENT

The Spotlight Effect

Cool, now that you're familiar with the law of detachment let's take this a step further and talk about **the Spotlight Effect.**

It might be that you're **struggling with anxiety that extends to all of your relationships** or that you feel **generalized anxiety about most of your interactions.**

Ever walked into a room and **felt like all eyes are on you—and not in a good way?**

Ever obsessed over **a tiny mistake you made** or get that **weird body jolt** when you think about something **cringey that you said?**

You're not alone, but you're also probably **overestimating how much attention people are actually paying to you.**

This psychological phenomenon is called the **"Spotlight Effect."**

The Spotlight Effect is this sense **that everyone is thinking about and judging you.**

You are the centre of your world - true.

But here's the eye-opening truth: **most people are too wrapped up in their own worlds to be thinking about you.**

Understanding the Spotlight Effect **can be liberating.**

Imagine the amount of emotional energy you could save by **not fussing over what people think.**

It's not about becoming careless or insensitive; it's about **freeing yourself from the bondage of external judgments.**

By recognizing that you're not the star of everyone else's show, **you unshackle yourself from unnecessary stress and social anxiety.**

Do whatever you want, be whoever you want.

Everyone is so caught up in their own lives that **not giving a f*ck really is the key.**

YOUR SHADOW WORK JOURNAL

YOUR SHADOW WORK JOURNAL

Now that you **understand disorganized attachment** a little better, you've become **aware of your thoughts** and you understand the **law of detachment**, it's time to get to the good part - shadow work.

What is the Shadow Self?

We all have a "shadow self"; this is the part of the subconscious mind where we store all of our **deepest shame, regret, denial and desires**.

It's the part of us that we hide from the world. In the context of **disorganized attachment style,** the shadow may include fears of **abandonment, disloyalty and disapproval.**

The more we repress these parts of ourselves **the darker our shadow self becomes**.

These emotional blockages lead to **self sabotaging behaviour, anxiety and negativity.**

Shadow work helps to **access these parts of yourself** to experience a release of these **repressed feelings.**

What is Shadow Work?

Shadow work is a simple but powerful practice where you **answer questions** relating to your childhood and adult life to **determine your patterns of behaviour.**

It was first derived by renowned psychoanalyst Carl Jung who believed that our shadow self is **predominantly developed during childhood**.

Prompts about **childhood are integral to the practice** to understand where your behaviour manifests from.

These prompts will help to access parts of the subconscious brain that store your **deepest memories, beliefs and assumptions about the world.**

These are the traits that are deeply programmed in the mind that you **barely even recognize in yourself**. As you answer the prompts you will unearth answers that **you might not have even been aware of.**

YOUR SHADOW WORK JOURNAL

The Role of Trauma

Now that you're aware of what shadow work is, you've probably realized that you'll be **confronting some past trauma** with your shadow work prompts.

It's important here to understand the context of **the word "trauma"** as we're using it.

Big "T" Trauma

"Big T" traumas include events that are generally recognized as traumatic by society. They're usually **significant, shocking, or catastrophic** occurrences such as emotional or sexual abuse, violence, or other life-threatening situations.

Small "t" Trauma

"Small t" traumas might not be life-threatening or as immediately shocking, but they still carry a **significant emotional weight**.

They include things like when a child is **emotionally neglected, dismissed, confused about their identity, overly disciplined, limited in expression, controlled, smothered, had too many expectations placed on them** or **were passively bullied** by their parent/s.

Maybe your parent/s were just **too busy trying to support the family,** maybe they were **trying their best but also struggling with their own issues.**

The terms "big T" and "small t" **do not imply** that one type of trauma is more important or impactful than the other.

The impact of trauma is subjective and **varies greatly from person to person**. Both types can lead to lasting emotional pain that affect you into adulthood.

Understanding these **root causes is crucial for healing**.

It allows you to recognize that **your coping mechanisms served a purpose** at one point, even if they're **no longer serving you now.**

It's **not about assigning blame,** but about **understanding and compassion.**

YOUR SHADOW WORK JOURNAL

Now that we've delved into the concept of shadow work, **it's time to put theory into practice.**

This section is designed to help you **explore your 'shadow'** through a series of prompts.

Each set of prompts focuses on a **different aspect of your relationship and personal history**.

1. Childhood Reflection
2. Self Perception & Self Worth
3. Fear & Defence Mechanisms
4. Relationships, Sex & Intimacy
5. Envisioning the Future

Remember, shadow work is a **personal and often emotional process**. It's okay to feel uncomfortable at times.

That discomfort is a sign that you're **pushing your boundaries and growing.**

YOUR SHADOW WORK JOURNAL

Shadow work journaling can be **quite an emotional experience** so we recommend practicing in a **safe and calm environment.**

Tips For Shadow Work Journalling

1. **Create a safe space:** Find a quiet and comfortable space where you can focus on your thoughts and emotions without distractions.Set up your space so that you feel calm and safe.
2. **Write Freely:** This journal is a judgement-free zone. Let your thoughts flow freely on the pages. Don't worry about sounding 'correct' or 'proper'. Just write what feels right for you, in your own voice.
3. **Choose prompts that resonate with you:** If they make you feel uncomfortable then they're usually the ones you should answer.
4. **Focus on the Details**: Go into as much detail as you can when writing your answers
5. **Don't hold back:** This journal is just for you, there should be no shame or fear when practicing. You don't have to share it with anyone unless you want to. It's a safe container for your thoughts, emotions, dreams, fears, and hopes.
6. **No Wrong Answers:** In this journal, every answer is the right one because it's yours. Your experiences, your feelings, your perspectives – they all matter. Each prompt is an invitation for self-exploration, not a test.
7. **Allow emotions to surface:** If you feel any intense emotions bubbling let them out!
8. **Embrace Creativity:** Feel free to use different forms of creative expression. If words don't feel sufficient, you can draw, sketch, doodle, use colors, write poems, or even create a collage. This journal is your canvas.
9. **Consistency and Flexibility:** You can practice over days, weeks or months. Aim for consistency, but don't stress if life gets hectic and you miss a day or two. The important thing is to come back when you can. Similarly, if you want to spend more time on a particular exercise, alter the question or skip one that doesn't resonate, that's perfectly fine. This journey is about you and should be adapted to your rhythm.
10. **Be kind to yourself:** if it feels overwhelming take a break.

CHILDHOOD
REFLECTION

CHILDHOOD REFLECTION

Shadow Work & Your Inner Child

Your shadow work journey starts with some **deep childhood reflection**. This is going to help you understand **where your avoidant patterns of behavior started.**

Your inner child is that part of your psyche that **still reacts and feels like the child you once were.**

It carries your **experiences, memories, and emotions** from your early years.

As we grow older, many of us suppress this part of ourselves to fit into societal norms and expectations, leading to an **unaddressed emotional turmoil** that can have a significant impact on our lives.

Shadow work is the process of **acknowledging, understanding, and healing this hidden part of yourself.**

It involves **addressing the unmet needs, unrecognized desires, and unresolved emotions of your inner child.**

By engaging in this profound self-reflection process, you can **identify the origins of your fears, insecurities, and patterns of behavior** that may be holding you back.

Shadow work can help us understand these experiences, **see how they shaped our attachment styles**, and allow us to **heal and move towards a healthier way of relating to others.**

Ready to get started?

CHILDHOOD REFLECTION

WHAT DID YOU THINK ABOUT YOUR PARENT/S' RELATIONSHIP GROWING UP? WRITE ABOUT THEM FROM YOUR CHILDHOOD PERSPECTIVE.

_____

_____

_____

_____

_____

_____

_____

_____

WHAT DO YOU THINK OF THEIR RELATIONSHIP AS AN ADULT?

_____

_____

_____

_____

_____

_____

_____

_____

CHILDHOOD REFLECTION

WHEN WAS THE FIRST TIME YOU REMEMBER BEING DISAPPOINTED BY SOMEONE GROWING UP? WHAT HAPPENED?

_____

_____

_____

_____

_____

_____

_____

_____

_____

_____

HOW DID THIS CHANGE THE WAY YOU LOOKED AT THAT PERSON?

_____

_____

_____

_____

_____

_____

_____

CHILDHOOD REFLECTION

WHEN YOU ACHIEVED ANYTHING AS A CHILD DID YOUR PARENT/S
ENCOURAGE AND VALIDATE YOUR ACHIEVEMENT? GIVE AN EXAMPLE OF
A TIME YOUR PARENTS CELEBRATED YOU.

_____

_____

_____

_____

_____

_____

_____

DID YOU FEEL SUPPORTED OR DID YOU FEEL PRESSURED?

_____

_____

_____

_____

HOW DO YOU THINK THIS AFFECTED YOU AS A CHILD?

_____

_____

_____

CHILDHOOD REFLECTION

DID YOU HAVE SOMEONE TO TURN TO WHEN YOU NEEDED COMFORT? WHO WERE THEY AND HOW DID THEY COMFORT YOU?

_____

_____

_____

_____

_____

_____

_____

_____

WHAT DID THAT MEAN TO YOU?

_____

_____

_____

_____

WHY DID YOU TRUST THIS PERSON?

_____

_____

_____

_____

CHILDHOOD REFLECTION

REMEMBER SPECIFICALLY TO WHEN YOU WERE 12 YEARS OLD. WRITE
ABOUT A DAY IN YOUR LIFE. TRY TO BE AS DETAILED AS POSSIBLE FROM
WHEN YOU WOKE UP TO WHEN YOU WENT TO BED. WHAT CAN YOU
REMEMBER?

CHILDHOOD REFLECTION

DID YOUR PARENT/S OPENLY DISCUSS STRESSES OR COMPLAIN (RELATIONSHIP, FINANCIAL, FAMILY)? WHAT DO YOU REMEMBER THEM TALKING ABOUT IN FRONT OF YOU?

_____

_____

_____

_____

_____

_____

_____

_____

_____

DID THIS WAY OF THINKING RUB OFF ON YOU? EXPLAIN WHY/ WHY NOT.

_____

_____

_____

_____

_____

_____

_____

_____

CHILDHOOD REFLECTION

WHAT WAS THE BIGGEST SECRET YOU KEPT AS A CHILD?

_____

_____

_____

_____

_____

_____

_____

_____

_____

HOW DID KEEPING THAT SECRET SHAPE YOU?

_____

_____

_____

_____

_____

_____

CHILDHOOD REFLECTION

WHAT WERE THE HIDDEN PRESSURES YOU FELT YOU HAD TO LIVE UP
TO AS A CHILD?

_____

_____

_____

_____

_____

_____

_____

HOW DO YOU THINK THESE PRESSURES SHAPED YOU?

_____

_____

_____

_____

DO YOU STILL FEEL THIS PRESSURE? IF SO, WHY?

_____

_____

_____

_____

CHILDHOOD REFLECTION

DID YOU HAVE AN ANXIOUS PARENT? IF SO, HOW DO YOU THINK THEIR ANXIETY AFFECTED YOU AS A CHILD?

_____

_____

_____

_____

_____

_____

_____

HOW DID THEIR REACTIONS TRIGGER YOU?

_____

_____

_____

_____

_____

CAN YOU RECONIZE ANY OF THEIR PATTERNS IN YOU? IF SO, WHAT?

_____

_____

_____

_____

CHILDHOOD REFLECTION

DID YOU HAVE A PARENT WITH MENTAL HEALTH ISSUES? IF SO, HOW DO YOU THINK IT AFFECTED YOU AS A CHILD?

_____
_____
_____
_____
_____
_____
_____

HOW DID THEIR REACTIONS TRIGGER YOU?

_____
_____
_____
_____

CAN YOU RECONIZE ANY OF THEIR PATTERNS IN YOU? IF SO, WHAT?

_____
_____
_____
_____

CHILDHOOD REFLECTION

DO YOU EVER REMEMBER FEELING INSECURE AS A CHILD? WHAT WAS HAPPENING AROUND YOU?

_____

_____

_____

_____

_____

DID YOU HAVE SUPPORT? IF SO, FROM WHO; IF NOT WHY NOT?

_____

_____

_____

_____

_____

HOW DO YOU THINK IT STILL AFFECTS YOU AS AN ADULT?

_____

_____

_____

_____

CHILDHOOD REFLECTION

WHEN YOU THINK ABOUT YOUR BOND WITH YOUR MOTHER/MOTHER FIGURE, WHAT STANDS OUT? HOW DID YOU FEEL ABOUT HER AS A CHILD?

_____

_____

_____

_____

_____

_____

_____

_____

_____

CAN YOU SEE ANY OF HER TRAITS IN YOU NOW? ARE THEY GOOD, BAD OR BOTH?

_____

_____

_____

_____

_____

_____

_____

_____

CHILDHOOD REFLECTION

WHEN YOU THINK ABOUT YOUR BOND WITH YOUR FATHER/FATHER FIGURE, WHAT STANDS OUT? HOW DID YOU FEEL ABOUT HIM AS A CHILD?

_____

_____

_____

_____

_____

_____

_____

CAN YOU SEE ANY OF HIS TRAITS IN YOU NOW? ARE THEY GOOD, BAD OR BOTH?

_____

_____

_____

_____

_____

_____

CHILDHOOD REFLECTION

REFLECT ON WHAT WAS YOUR MOST TRAUMATIC EXPERIENCE AS A CHILD. WHAT HAPPENED?

_____

_____

_____

_____

_____

_____

_____

_____

_____

HOW DID THIS MAKE YOU FEEL ABOUT YOURSELF? DID IT CHANGE YOU? HOW?

_____

_____

_____

_____

_____

_____

_____

_____

CHILDHOOD REFLECTION

WHAT WAS YOUR HAPPIEST MOMENT AS A CHILD - WHERE WERE YOU, WHO WERE YOU WITH? EXPLAIN IN DETAIL.

_____

_____

_____

_____

_____

_____

_____

_____

_____

HOW DID YOU FEEL LOVED IN THIS MOMENT, IF AT ALL?

_____

_____

_____

_____

_____

_____

_____

_____

CHILDHOOD REFLECTION

IF YOUR 10 YEAR OLD SELF COULD EXPLAIN HOW THEY WERE FEELING, WHAT WOULD THEY SAY? WRITE IT IN THEIR TONE OF VOICE.

_____

_____

_____

_____

_____

_____

_____

_____

_____

_____

_____

_____

_____

_____

_____

_____

_____

_____

CHILDHOOD REFLECTION

WERE THERE ANY SPECIFIC PHYSICAL FEATURES THAT MADE YOU FEEL INSECURE WHEN YOU WERE YOUNGER? WHAT WERE THEY?

_____

_____

_____

_____

_____

_____

_____

DO YOU REMEMBER WHAT TRIGGERED THIS INSECURITY?

_____

_____

_____

_____

HAS THIS CHANGED OR ARE YOU STILL STRUGGLING WITH IT? WHY/WHY NOT?

_____

_____

_____

_____

CHILDHOOD REFLECTION

HOW DID YOUR PARENT/S REACT WHEN YOU EXPRESSED YOUR NEEDS AS A CHILD? GIVE A SPECIFIC EXAMPLE OF A TIME THEY REACTED TO YOU EXPRESSING YOUR NEEDS.

_____

_____

_____

_____

_____

_____

_____

_____

CAN YOU REMEMBER HOW THEY MADE YOU FEEL? EXPLAIN IN DETAIL.

_____

_____

_____

_____

_____

_____

_____

_____

_____

CHILDHOOD REFLECTION

DRAW A MAP OF YOUR CHILDHOOD NEIGHBOURHOOD. LABEL THE
PLACES THAT WERE IMPORTANT TO YOU AND WRITE A
DESCRIPTION OF WHAT THEY MEANT TO YOU ON THE NEXT PAGE.

CHILDHOOD REFLECTION

WHAT DID THESE PLACES MEAN TO YOU?

CHILDHOOD REFLECTION

DO YOU SHARE THE SAME VALUES AS YOUR PARENT/S AS AN ADULT OR HAVE YOU GONE IN THE OPPOSITE DIRECTION? WHAT VALUES ARE THEY AND WHY?

CHILDHOOD REFLECTION

WERE THERE EVER TIMES WHEN YOU FELT LIKE YOU HAD TO HIDE OR
CHANGE PARTS OF YOURSELF FROM YOUR FAMILY? WHAT WERE
THEY?

_____

_____

_____

_____

_____

_____

_____

_____

ARE YOU STILL HIDING PARTS OF YOURSELF? IF SO, WHY?

_____

_____

_____

_____

_____

_____

_____

CHILDHOOD REFLECTION

IF YOUR CHILDHOOD SELF COULD EXPLAIN HOW THEY FELT ABOUT YOUR
SIBLINGS, WHAT WOULD THEY SAY? WRITE IT IN THEIR TONE OF VOICE.

_____

_____

_____

_____

_____

_____

_____

_____

HOW DO YOU FEEL ABOUT THEM NOW? ARE YOU CLOSE? DO YOU
WISH YOU WERE CLOSER?

_____

_____

_____

_____

_____

_____

_____

CHILDHOOD REFLECTION

WERE YOU EVER BULLIED OR DISMISSED BY YOUR SIBLINGS? TELL A STORY ABOUT A TIME YOU FELT THIS.

_____

_____

_____

_____

_____

_____

_____

_____

_____

DID THIS BULLYING EVER MAKE YOU FEEL UNWANTED OR LIKE A BURDEN? DO YOU FEEL LIKE THIS STILL? WHY?

_____

_____

_____

_____

_____

_____

_____

_____

CHILDHOOD REFLECTION

WHAT ATTACHMENT STYLE DO YOU THINK YOUR PARENT/S HAVE TO TOWARD <u>YOU</u>? IS IT HEALTHY?

_____

_____

_____

_____

_____

_____

_____

_____

_____

_____

_____

IS THIS FEELING THE SAME AS AN ADULT? WHY/WHY NOT?

_____

_____

_____

_____

_____

_____

CHILDHOOD REFLECTION

DRAW SOMETHING THAT YOUR CHILDHOOD SELF USED TO DRAW. EVEN IF YOU'RE TERRIBLE AT IT, GET CREATIVE AND HAVE A LITTLE FUN.

CHILDHOOD REFLECTION

AS A CHILD WHAT'S ONE THING YOU WISH YOU COULD HAVE OPENED UP ABOUT TO YOUR PARENT/S?

_____

_____

_____

_____

_____

_____

_____

_____

_____

WHY DID YOU FEAR TELLING THEM?

_____

_____

_____

_____

_____

_____

_____

CHILDHOOD REFLECTION

REFLECT ON A TIME IN YOUR CHILDHOOD WHERE YOU FELT THE NEED TO SUPPRESS YOUR EMOTIONS. WHAT WAS HAPPENING TO YOU DURING THIS TIME?

_____

_____

_____

_____

_____

_____

_____

_____

_____

WHY DID YOU FEEL THE NEED TO HIDE YOUR TRUE FEELINGS?

_____

_____

_____

_____

_____

_____

_____

_____

_____

CHILDHOOD REFLECTION

WHAT WAS ONE STRONG BELIEF THAT YOU HAD AS A CHILD THAT YOU WERE WRONG ABOUT.

_____

_____

_____

_____

_____

WHAT CHANGED YOUR MIND?

_____

_____

_____

HAVE YOU FULLY RELEASED THIS BELIEF OR DO YOU THINK IT STILL LINGERS? WHY?

_____

_____

_____

_____

_____

_____

CHILDHOOD REFLECTION

DID YOU HAVE ANY CHILDHOOD EXPERIENCES THAT LED YOU TO FEAR BEING DEPENDANT ON SOMEONE? WHO WAS IT? DID THEY LET YOU DOWN?

_____

_____

_____

_____

_____

_____

_____

_____

_____

_____

HOW DO YOU THINK THIS IMPACTS YOUR WILLINGNESS TO ASK PEOPLE FOR HELP AS AN ADULT?

_____

_____

_____

_____

_____

_____

_____

CHILDHOOD REFLECTION

THINK ABOUT A CHILDHOOD DREAM THAT YOU HAD? WHAT DID YOU ENVISION YOUR LIFE TO BE LIKE?

_____

_____

_____

_____

_____

_____

_____

_____

HOW DID THINGS TURN OUT DIFFERENTLY? WHAT'S SOMETHING YOU WISH YOU DID?

_____

_____

_____

_____

_____

_____

_____

CHILDHOOD REFLECTION

WHAT WERE YOU TAUGHT
ABOUT LOVE GROWING UP?

_____

_____

_____

_____

_____

HOW DO YOU THINK YOUR PARENT/S OPINIONS HAVE AFFECTED YOU?

_____

_____

_____

_____

_____

_____

HOW CAN YOU LET GO OF ANY BELIEFS THAT NO LONGER SERVE YOU?

_____

_____

_____

_____

CHILDHOOD REFLECTION

DID YOU FEEL LIKE YOU HAD TO GROW UP QUICKLY AND TAKE CARE OF YOURSELF (LITERALLY OR EMOTIONALLY)? EXPLAIN.

_____

_____

_____

_____

_____

_____

_____

_____

HOW DID THAT MAKE YOU FEEL AS A CHILD? HOW DID YOU COPE?

_____

_____

_____

_____

_____

_____

_____

_____

_____

CHILDHOOD REFLECTION

DID YOU EVER FEEL SMOTHERED OR CONTROLLED BY YOUR PARENT/S GROWING UP? EXPLAIN.

_____

_____

_____

_____

_____

_____

_____

_____

HOW DO YOU THINK THIS AFFECTS YOUR RELATIONSHIPS AS AN ADULT?

_____

_____

_____

_____

_____

_____

_____

_____

CHILDHOOD REFLECTION

WRITE ABOUT A TIME THAT YOUR HOME FELT CHAOTIC AS A CHILD. WHAT WAS HAPPENING? HOW DID YOU REACT?

_____

_____

_____

_____

_____

_____

_____

_____

AS AN ADULT DO YOU FEEL LIKE YOU ALWAYS WANT TO BE IN CONTROL? IF SO, WHY DO YOU THINK THAT IS?

_____

_____

_____

_____

_____

_____

_____

_____

_____

CHILDHOOD REFLECTION

WHAT ATTACHMENT STYLE DO YOU THINK YOUR PARENT/S HAD <u>TO EACH OTHER?</u> WHY?

_____

_____

_____

_____

_____

_____

_____

DO YOU THINK THEIR RELATIONSHIP DYNAMIC WAS HEALTHY AS AN ADULT?

_____

_____

_____

_____

_____

_____

_____

_____

_____

_____

CHILDHOOD REFLECTION

IMAGINE YOU COULD TRAVEL BACK IN TIME TO YOUR CHILDHOOD FOR ONE DAY. WRITE ABOUT WHAT YOU WOULD DO, WHO YOU WOULD SEE, AND WHAT YOU WOULD SAY TO THEM.

_____

_____

_____

_____

_____

_____

_____

_____

_____

_____

_____

_____

_____

_____

_____

_____

_____

_____

_____

_____

_____

_____

CHILDHOOD REFLECTION

DID YOU RELY HEAVILY ON ONE PARENT OR FEEL CODDLED BY THEM? OR DID YOU CRAVE A PARENT/S ATTENTION WHO DIDN'T GIVE IT TO YOU? EXPLAIN.

_____

_____

_____

_____

_____

_____

_____

_____

_____

_____

HOW DID THIS RELATIONSHIP IMPACT THE WAY YOU LOOK AT CLOSENESS IN RELATIONSHIPS?

_____

_____

_____

_____

_____

_____

CHILDHOOD REFLECTION

CREATE A PLAYLIST THAT REPRESENTS SONGS YOU LOVED AS A KID.
LISTEN TO IT AND WRITE ABOUT HOW THE PLAYLIST MAKES YOU FEEL AND
WHAT IT REMINDS YOU OF.

CHILDHOOD REFLECTION

CAN YOU RECALL A MOMENT AS A CHILD WHERE YOU FELT A STRONG SENSE OF SHAME OR GUILT? WHAT HAPPENED?

_____

_____

_____

_____

_____

_____

HOW DO YOU THINK THIS IMPACTED THE WAY YOU ACTED AS A CHILD?

_____

_____

_____

_____

_____

DO YOU THINK THIS SHAME OR GUILT STILL LINGERS? WHY?

_____

_____

_____

_____

CHILDHOOD REFLECTION

WAS THERE SOMEONE YOU LOOKED UP TO AS A CHILD? WHO WERE THEY AND WHY DID YOU LOOK UP TO THEM?

_____

_____

_____

_____

_____

DID THEY ALWAYS COME THROUGH FOR YOU OR WERE YOU EVER DISAPPOINTED? HOW DO YOU THINK THIS AFFECTED YOU?

_____

_____

_____

_____

_____

DO YOU STILL LOOK UP TO THIS PERSON AS AN ADULT? WHY/ WHY NOT?

_____

_____

_____

_____

CHILDHOOD REFLECTION

DID YOUR PARENT/S HAVE ENOUGH TIME FOR YOU? REFLECT ON A TIME
WHERE YOU REMEMBER YOUR PARENT/S BEING PRESENT AND HAVING
FUN WITH YOU.

_____

_____

_____

_____

_____

_____

_____

_____

HOW DID YOU FEEL WHEN THEY DIDN'T HAVE TIME FOR YOU? DID
YOU EVER FEEL DISMISSED OR LIKE A NUISANCE? EXPLAIN.

_____

_____

_____

_____

_____

_____

_____

CHILDHOOD REFLECTION

WHAT ROLE DID YOU PLAY IN YOUR FRIENDSHIP GROUPS? EXPLAIN YOUR PERSONALITY AT SCHOOL.

_____

_____

_____

_____

_____

_____

_____

_____

HOW DID THIS AFFECT YOUR SELF PERCEPTION?

_____

_____

_____

_____

_____

_____

_____

CHILDHOOD REFLECTION

DID YOUR SIBLINGS OR FRIENDS EVER MAKE ANY COMMENTS ABOUT YOUR LOOKS THAT HAVE STUCK WITH YOU? WHAT DID THEY SAY?

_____

_____

_____

_____

_____

_____

HOW HAVE THOSE COMMENTS SHAPED YOUR PERCEPTION OF YOURSELF?

_____

_____

_____

_____

_____

DOES IT STILL AFFECT YOU? WHY?

_____

_____

_____

_____

CHILDHOOD REFLECTION

WRITE A LETTER TO YOUR MOTHER/MOTHER FIGURE ABOUT YOUR CHILDHOOD, WHAT DO YOU WANT THEM TO KNOW ABOUT HOW YOU FELT?

CHILDHOOD REFLECTION

WRITE A LETTER TO YOUR FATHER/FATHER FIGURE ABOUT YOUR
CHILDHOOD, WHAT DO YOU WANT THEM TO KNOW ABOUT HOW
YOU FELT AS A CHILD?

CHILDHOOD REFLECTION

IF YOU COULD SAY ANYTHING TO SOMEONE FROM YOUR
CHILDHOOD, WHAT WOULD IT BE? WRITE IT DOWN AND DONT
HOLD BACK.

CHILDHOOD REFLECTION

IMAGINE MEETING YOUR 8 YEAR OLD SELF. PICTURE IT VIVIDLY.
WHERE WOULD YOU MEET THEM? WHAT ADVICE WOULD YOU GIVE
THEM? WRITE IT OUT AS IF YOU'RE SPEAKING TO THEM.

CHILDHOOD REFLECTION

IF YOUR CHILDHOOD SELF COULD SEE YOU NOW, WHAT WOULD THEY THINK? WOULD THEY BE SURPRISED AT WHO YOU HAVE BECOME? WHY?

_____

_____

_____

_____

_____

_____

_____

_____

WHAT WOULD YOUR CHILDHOOD SELF WANT FOR YOU? WRITE IN THEIR TONE OF VOICE.

_____

_____

_____

_____

_____

_____

_____

SELF PERCEPTION & SELF WORTH

SELF PERCEPTION & SELF WORTH

WHAT DOES YOUR INNER NARRATIVE SOUND LIKE? HOW DO YOU TALK TO YOURSELF WHEN YOU'RE ALONE?

_____

_____

_____

_____

_____

_____

WHAT'S A RECURRENT THOUGHT THAT YOU HAVE, SOMETHING THAT POPS UP RANDOMLY? EXPLAIN IT.

_____

_____

_____

_____

_____

WHY DO YOU THINK THAT THIS COMES UP SO OFTEN?

_____

_____

_____

_____

SELF PERCEPTION & SELF WORTH

DO YOU FEEL COMFORTABLE HAVING DEEP CONVERSATIONS ABOUT YOURSELF? WHEN IT'S TIME TO TALK ABOUT <u>YOU</u> DO YOU OPEN UP? WHY?

_____

_____

_____

_____

_____

_____

_____

_____

_____

WHAT'S HOLDING YOU BACK? CAN YOU PINPOINT WHAT YOU'RE AFRAID OF?

_____

_____

_____

_____

_____

_____

_____

_____

SELF PERCEPTION & SELF WORTH

WHAT HAPPENS IN MOMENTS WHERE SOMEONE IS BEING VULNERABLE
WITH YOU AND EXPECTING IT BACK? WRITE ABOUT THE LAST TIME THIS
HAPPENED. WHAT DID THEY SAY AND WHAT DID YOU SAY IN RESPONSE?

SELF PERCEPTION & SELF WORTH

DO YOU OFTEN FEEL LIKE YOU'RE NOT GOOD ENOUGH OR FEAR BEING PERCEIVED AS A FAILURE? WHY?

_____

_____

_____

_____

_____

_____

_____

_____

WHY DO OTHER PEOPLE'S OPINIONS OF YOU MATTER? IS THERE SOMEONE YOU'RE TRYING TO IMPRESS? IF SO, WHO?

_____

_____

_____

_____

_____

_____

_____

_____

_____

SELF PERCEPTION & SELF WORTH

DRAW LINES RADIATING FROM THE CIRCLE LISTING THINGS YOU FEEL
INSECURE ABOUT. WHEN YOU'RE DONE TAKE A SECOND TO REFLECT ON
WHAT YOU'VE WRITTEN, THEN SCRIBBLE ALL OVER IT.

Insecurities

SELF PERCEPTION & SELF WORTH

WRITE DOWN A LIST OF THE PHYSICAL FEATURES YOU LOVE ABOUT YOURSELF AND THE ONE'S THAT YOU DON'T LIKE

LOVE

_____

_____

_____

_____

_____

_____

_____

_____

_____

DON'T LIKE

_____

_____

_____

_____

_____

_____

_____

_____

SELF PERCEPTION & SELF WORTH

WRITE DOWN A LIST OF THE PERSONALITY TRAITS YOU LOVE ABOUT YOURSELF AND THE ONE'S THAT YOU DON'T LIKE

LOVE

_____

_____

_____

_____

_____

_____

_____

_____

DON'T LIKE

_____

_____

_____

_____

_____

_____

_____

SELF PERCEPTION & SELF WORTH

HOW CAN YOU WORK ON THE THINGS THAT YOU LISTED THAT YOU "DON'T LIKE" ABOUT YOURSELF?

SELF PERCEPTION & SELF WORTH

DO YOU CHANGE YOUR PERSONALITY TO FIT IN WITH DIFFERENT PEOPLE? IS IT TO MAKE THEM MORE COMFORTABLE OR YOU? WHAT ABOUT YOU DO YOU CHANGE AND WHY?

_____

_____

_____

_____

_____

_____

_____

_____

WHY IS IT HARD FOR YOU TO BE YOURSELF?

_____

_____

_____

_____

_____

_____

_____

_____

_____

SELF PERCEPTION & SELF WORTH

WHAT STRENGTHS DO YOU OFTEN DOWNPLAY OR IGNORE ABOUT
YOURSELF? WRITE ABOUT THIS STRENGTH AND WHY YOU'RE SO
GOOD AT IT.

_____

_____

_____

_____

_____

_____

_____

_____

_____

WHY DO YOU IGNORE OR DOWNPLAY IT? HOW CAN YOU LEAN
INTO IT MORE?

_____

_____

_____

_____

_____

_____

_____

_____

SELF PERCEPTION & SELF WORTH

WHAT IS THE HARSHEST CRITICISM YOU OFTEN GIVE TO YOURSELF? WHAT'S SOMETHING NEGATIVE THAT YOU'VE SAID ABOUT YOURSELF TIME AND TIME AGAIN. WRITE IT DOWN.

_____

_____

_____

_____

_____

_____

_____

_____

_____

READ THAT BACK. IS IT ACTUALLY TRUE OR ARE YOU BEING HARD ON YOURSELF? HOW CAN YOU SHIFT THIS BELIEF ABOUT YOU?

_____

_____

_____

_____

_____

_____

SELF PERCEPTION & SELF WORTH

WRITE ABOUT AN ACHIEVEMENT THAT YOU DOWNPLAYED OR DISMISSED.

_____

_____

_____

_____

_____

_____

_____

_____

_____

WHY DO YOU FND IT HARD TO CELEBRATE YOURSELF?

_____

_____

_____

_____

_____

_____

_____

SELF PERCEPTION & SELF WORTH

DESCRIBE A MOMENT WHERE YOU FELT THE NEED TO PROVE YOUR WORTH TO SOMEONE. HOW DID THEY RESPOND? WHAT HAPPENED?

_____

_____

_____

_____

_____

_____

_____

_____

_____

WHAT EMOTIONS DID THIS TRIGGER FOR YOU?

_____

_____

_____

_____

_____

_____

_____

SELF PERCEPTION & SELF WORTH

WRITE DOWN AN EXPERIENCE WHERE YOU FELT YOUR SELF-WORTH WAS TIED TO EXTERNAL VALIDATION. WHAT WAS HAPPENING AND WHO'S VALIDATION WERE YOU CHASING?

_____

_____

_____

_____

_____

_____

_____

_____

WHY DID THEIR VALIDATION MATTER TO YOU?

_____

_____

_____

_____

HOW DOES VALIDATION SHAPE YOUR INTERACTIONS AND RELATIONSHIPS?

_____

_____

_____

_____

SELF PERCEPTION & SELF WORTH

THINK ABOUT A TIME WHEN YOUR NEGATIVE BELIEFS ABOUT YOURSELF HELD YOU BACK. WHAT DID YOU HOLD BACK FROM?

_____

_____

_____

_____

_____

_____

_____

_____

HOW WOULD THINGS HAVE BEEN DIFFERENT IF YOU HAD A MORE POSITIVE SELF-VIEW?

_____

_____

_____

_____

_____

_____

_____

SELF PERCEPTION & SELF WORTH

**WHEN'S THE LAST TIME YOU SELF SABOTAGED?
TELL THE STORY**

_____

_____

_____

_____

_____

_____

WHY DID YOU DO IT?

_____

_____

_____

_____

_____

WHAT WOULD YOU DO DIFFERENTLY NOW?

_____

_____

_____

_____

SELF PERCEPTION & SELF WORTH

IF YOU HAD A FRIEND WHO SPOKE TO YOU IN THE SAME WAY THAT
YOU SOMETIMES SPEAK TO YOURSELF, HOW LONG WOULD YOU ALLOW
THIS PERSON TO BE YOUR FRIEND? EXPLAIN WHY.

_____

_____

_____

_____

_____

_____

_____

_____

_____

HOW CAN YOU MAKE CHANGES ABOUT THE WAY YOU THINK ABOUT
YOURSELF & YOUR SUBCONSCIOUS LOOP? ARE YOU PRACTICING MIRROR
WORK?

_____

_____

_____

_____

_____

_____

SELF PERCEPTION & SELF WORTH

HOW DOES YOUR PHYSICAL APPEARANCE AFFECT YOUR SELF-WORTH AND SELF-PERCEPTION?

_____

_____

_____

_____

_____

_____

_____

IS THERE ANYTHING YOU WANT TO CHANGE? WHY?

_____

_____

_____

_____

WHAT STEPS CAN YOU START TAKING TOWARD FEELING MORE CONFIDENT?

_____

_____

_____

_____

SELF PERCEPTION & SELF WORTH

HOW DO YOU WANT TO PERCEIVE YOURSELF AND BE PERCEIVED BY OTHERS?
WRITE DOWN A DETAILED DESCRIPTION OF THE BEST VERSION OF YOU. WHO
ARE YOU? WHAT DO YOU LOOK LIKE? WHAT ARE YOU DOING?

SELF PERCEPTION & SELF WORTH

HAVE YOU EVER FELT LIKE A PARTNER DIDN'T TRULY UNDERSTAND YOU OR YOUR NEEDS? IF SO, WHAT WERE YOUR NEEDS?

_____

_____

_____

_____

_____

_____

_____

_____

_____

HOW DID YOU COMMUNICATE ABOUT IT? WHAT COULD YOU HAVE DONE DIFFERENTLY?

_____

_____

_____

_____

WHAT COULD THEY HAVE DONE DIFFERENTLY?

_____

_____

_____

SELF PERCEPTION & SELF WORTH

HAVE YOU EVER CAUGHT YOURSELF COMPARING YOUR ABILITIES OR ACHIEVEMENTS TO SOMEONE ELSE'S? WRITE ABOUT A SITUATION WHERE YOU DID THIS.

_____

_____

_____

_____

_____

_____

HOW DOES COMPARISON AFFECT YOU? WHAT DOES IT MAKE YOU FEEL ABOUT YOURSELF?

_____

_____

_____

_____

_____

_____

WHAT STEPS CAN YOU TAKE TO STOP COMPARING YOURSELF TO OTHERS?

_____

_____

_____

SELF PERCEPTION & SELF WORTH

THINK ABOUT A MOMENT WHEN YOUR CONFIDENCE WAS SHAKEN. WHAT HAPPENED AND HOW DID YOU RESPOND?

_____

_____

_____

_____

_____

_____

_____

_____

DO YOU THINK THIS STILL AFFECTS YOU?

_____

_____

_____

_____

_____

HOW CAN YOU REFRAME THIS AND MOVE ON FROM IT?

_____

_____

_____

SELF PERCEPTION & SELF WORTH

WHEN YOU MEET SOMEONE NEW, HOW DO YOU THINK THEY PERCEIVE YOU? EXPLAIN YOU FROM THE PERSPECTIVE OF SOMEONE NEW.

_____

_____

_____

_____

_____

_____

_____

_____

_____

_____

_____

DO YOU THINK OTHERS WOULD VALIDATE YOUR OPINION?

_____

_____

_____

_____

_____

_____

SELF PERCEPTION & SELF WORTH

WHAT ARE THREE NEGATIVE BELIEFS YOU HAVE ABOUT YOURSELF? LIST THEM.

_____

_____

_____

_____

_____

_____

_____

_____

_____

_____

WHERE DO YOU THINK THESE CAME FROM?

_____

_____

_____

_____

_____

_____

SELF PERCEPTION & SELF WORTH

IS THERE ANYONE IN YOUR LIFE THAT STILL TREATS YOU LIKE A 'VERSION OF YOU' THAT NO LONGER EXISTS? WHO IS IT AND HOW DOES IT MAKE YOU FEEL?

_____

_____

_____

_____

_____

_____

_____

HOW CAN YOU EXPRESS TO THEM THAT YOU'VE CHANGED?

_____

_____

_____

_____

HOW CAN YOU LET GO IF THEY CAN'T CHANGE THEIR PERCEPTION OF YOU?

_____

_____

_____

SELF PERCEPTION & SELF WORTH

WHAT'S YOUR MOST TOXIC TRAIT?
EXPLAIN IN DETAIL.

_____

_____

_____

_____

_____

_____

_____

_____

_____

HOW WOULD YOU JUDGE SOMEONE ELSE WHO DOES THE SAME THING?
BE HONEST.

_____

_____

_____

_____

_____

_____

_____

_____

SELF PERCEPTION & SELF WORTH

HOW DO YOU REACT WHEN SOMEONE LEAVES YOU ON READ OR DOESN'T RESPOND QUICKLY TO A TEXT MESSAGE? CAN YOU WRITE DOWN EXACTLY WHAT GOES THROUGH YOUR MIND?

SELF PERCEPTION & SELF WORTH

WRITE ABOUT A MOMENT WHEN YOU FELT TRULY PROUD OF YOURSELF. WHAT HAPPENED?

_____

_____

_____

_____

_____

_____

_____

_____

_____

_____

_____

WHAT ABOUT THIS MOMENT FELT SPECIAL?

_____

_____

_____

_____

_____

SELF PERCEPTION & SELF WORTH

HOW WOULD IT FEEL TO FULLY EMBRACE YOUR SEXUALITY, FREE OF ANY INSECURITIES OR DOUBTS?

_____

_____

_____

_____

_____

_____

_____

_____

_____

_____

_____

WHAT'S HOLDING YOU BACK?

_____

_____

_____

_____

_____

SELF PERCEPTION & SELF WORTH

HAS ANYONE EVER POINTED OUT AN INSECURITY THAT YOU HADN'T NOTICED YOURSELF? WHAT WAS IT?

_____

_____

_____

_____

_____

_____

_____

_____

_____

_____

_____

HOW DID THAT MAKE YOU FEEL? IS IT STILL ON YOUR MIND? WHY?

_____

_____

_____

_____

_____

SELF PERCEPTION & SELF WORTH

HOW WOULD YOUR BEST FRIEND DESCRIBE YOU? WRITE IT OUT IN THEIR TONE OF VOICE.

_____

_____

_____

_____

_____

_____

_____

_____

_____

DO YOU AGREE WITH THEIR DESCRIPTION OF YOU?

_____

_____

_____

_____

_____

_____

_____

SELF PERCEPTION & SELF WORTH

THINK OF YOUR CLOSEST FRIEND - WHAT ADVICE WOULD YOU GIVE THEM ABOUT THEIR OWN INSECURITIES?

_____

_____

_____

_____

_____

_____

_____

_____

_____

_____

IS THIS GOOD AVICE FOR YOU TOO? WHY/WHY NOT?

_____

_____

_____

_____

_____

_____

_____

SELF PERCEPTION & SELF WORTH

WHAT ARE 3 PHYSICAL TRAITS THAT YOU LOVE ABOUT YOURSELF AND WHY?

_____

_____

_____

_____

_____

_____

_____

_____

_____

HOW CAN YOU SHOW THESE PARTS OF YOU MORE LOVE?

_____

_____

_____

_____

_____

_____

SELF PERCEPTION & SELF WORTH

IF A STRANGER WAS LOOKING AT YOU, WHAT WOULD THEY SEE? HOW WOULD THEY PERCEIVE YOU BASED ON LOOKS ALONE? EXPLAIN IN DETAIL.

WHY DO YOU THINK THIS? IS IT VALID?

SELF PERCEPTION & SELF WORTH

HOW HAVE YOUR INSECURITIES INFLUENCED HOW YOU FEEL ABOUT SEX AND INTIMACY?

_____

_____

_____

_____

_____

_____

_____

_____

_____

DO YOU HOLD BACK? IF SO, WHY? IF NOT, WHY NOT?

_____

_____

_____

_____

_____

_____

_____

SELF PERCEPTION & SELF WORTH

WHAT STEPS CAN YOU TAKE TO FEEL MORE POSITIVE ABOUT YOUR BODY IMAGE?

_____

_____

_____

_____

_____

_____

_____

_____

_____

WHAT ARE YOU DOING THIS WEEK TO MAKE IT HAPPEN?

_____

_____

_____

_____

_____

_____

_____

_____

SELF PERCEPTION & SELF WORTH

HOW DOES SOCIAL MEDIA IMPACT YOUR SELF PERCEPTION? HAS IT EVER TRIGGERED YOUR ANXIETY?

_____

_____

_____

_____

_____

_____

_____

_____

CAN YOU UNFOLLOW OR MUTE ACCOUNTS THAT MAKE YOU FEEL CRAPPY? HOW WOULD THAT MAKE YOU FEEL?

_____

_____

_____

_____

_____

_____

_____

_____

_____

_____

SELF PERCEPTION & SELF WORTH

WHAT ARE 3 PERSONALITY TRAITS THAT YOU LOVE ABOUT YOURSELF AND WHY?

_____

_____

_____

_____

_____

_____

_____

_____

_____

HOW CAN YOU MAKE THESE PARTS OF YOU SHINE MORE OFTEN?

_____

_____

_____

_____

_____

_____

_____

_____

_____

SELF PERCEPTION & SELF WORTH

THINK ABOUT THE LAST TIME YOU HAD A GOOD LAUGH. WHO WERE YOU WITH AND WHAT IS THE STORY?

_____

_____

_____

_____

_____

_____

_____

_____

_____

WHY WAS IT SO FUNNY? HOW DID THIS JOY MAKE YOU FEEL? HOW CAN YOU EXPERIENCE THIS MORE?

_____

_____

_____

_____

_____

_____

SELF PERCEPTION & SELF WORTH

WHAT GOES THROUGH YOUR HEAD ABOUT SOMEONE ON A FIRST DATE? WHAT ARE YOU TRYING TO ASSESS? EXPLAIN IN DETAIL.

SELF PERCEPTION & SELF WORTH

WRITE ABOUT A SPONTANEOUS ADVENTURE YOU ONCE HAD. WHAT WAS THE EXPERIENCE LIKE?

_____

_____

_____

_____

_____

_____

_____

_____

_____

HOW CAN YOU DO THIS MORE OFTEN?

_____

_____

_____

_____

_____

_____

SELF PERCEPTION & SELF WORTH

CONSIDER A TIME WHEN YOU COMPROMISED YOUR OWN NEEDS FOR
SOMEONE ELSE. WHAT HAPPENED?

_____

_____

_____

_____

_____

_____

_____

SHOULD YOU FOCUS ON PUTTING YOURSELF FIRST MORE? WHY/ WHY NOT?

_____

_____

_____

_____

_____

HOW CAN YOU PRACTICE PUTTING YOURSELF FIRST MORE? IF SO, HOW?

_____

_____

_____

_____

_____

SELF PERCEPTION & SELF WORTH

YOU'RE WORKING ON LETTING GO OF YOUR PAST TRAUMA, CAN YOU MAKE A NEW PLAYLIST FOR THIS ERA? AS YOU LISTEN TO IT WRITE ABOUT WHAT SONGS YOU CHOSE AND WHY.

SELF PERCEPTION & SELF WORTH

WRITE DOWN A LIST OF EVERYTHING YOU LOVE ABOUT YOUR PERSONALITY AND EVERYTHING THAT YOU WANT TO CHANGE

LOVE

_____

_____

_____

_____

_____

_____

_____

_____

_____

NEEDS A CHANGE

_____

_____

_____

_____

_____

_____

_____

_____

SELF PERCEPTION & SELF WORTH

REFLECT ON AN INSECURITY THAT YOU FEEL HAS DEFINED YOU OR
INFLUENCED YOUR LIFE CHOICES. WHAT IS IT, HOW DO YOU THINK
YOU DEVELOPED IT AND HOW HAS IT SHAPED YOUR EXPERIENCES?

_____

_____

_____

_____

_____

_____

_____

_____

_____

_____

_____

_____

_____

_____

_____

_____

_____

_____

_____

_____

_____

_____

SELF PERCEPTION & SELF WORTH

WHAT'S ONE THING THAT YOU'VE ALWAYS WANTED TO TRY BUT HAVEN'T YET?

_____

_____

_____

_____

_____

_____

WHAT'S STOPPING YOU?

_____

_____

_____

_____

_____

WHAT'S SOME STEPS YOU CAN TAKE TO DO IT?

_____

_____

_____

_____

SELF PERCEPTION & SELF WORTH

**WHAT IS A PIECE OF PERSONAL WISDOM YOU CARRY WITH
YOU AND WHO DID YOU LEARN IT FROM?**

_____

_____

_____

_____

_____

_____

_____

HOW DOES THIS SHAPE YOUR DECISIONS?

_____

_____

_____

WHEN'S THE LAST TIME YOU FOLLOWED THIS PIECE OF WISDOM?

_____

_____

_____

_____

SELF PERCEPTION & SELF WORTH

WHAT ARE YOU ABSOLUTELY TERRIFIED OF THAT YOU HAVEN'T EVER SHARED WITH ANYONE?

_____

_____

_____

_____

_____

_____

_____

WHAT'S THE WORST THAT COULD HAPPEN IF YOU DID?

_____

_____

_____

_____

_____

_____

_____

_____

_____

_____

SELF PERCEPTION & SELF WORTH

DO YOU REMEMBER A SPECIFIC MOMENT YOU REALIZED YOU'VE
GROWN AND CHANGED? DESCRIBE THAT MOMENT.

_____

_____

_____

_____

_____

_____

WHAT HELPED YOU TO ACHIEVE THAT GROWTH?

_____

_____

_____

_____

_____

WHAT DOES YOUR NEXT STEP TOWARD GROWTH ENTAIL?

_____

_____

_____

_____

SELF PERCEPTION & SELF WORTH

SHARE THE WEIRDEST THING ABOUT YOU.
WHAT'S THE STORY BEHIND IT?

_____

_____

_____

_____

_____

_____

_____

_____

WHAT DO YOU LOVE ABOUT THIS QUIRK?

_____

_____

_____

_____

_____

_____

_____

_____

_____

_____

SELF PERCEPTION & SELF WORTH

IMAGINE MEETING YOUR 16 YEAR OLD SELF. PICTURE IT VIVIDLY. WHERE WOULD YOU MEET? WHAT WOULD YOU WARN THEM AGAINST? WHAT ADVICE WOULD YOU GIVE? WRITE IT OUT.

FEAR &
DEFENCE
MECHANISMS

FEAR & DEFENCE MECHANISMS

DID YOU EVER SEE YOUR FATHER/FATHER FIGURE EMBRACE VULNERABILITY
GROWING UP? HOW DID HE PERCEIVE IT? HOW DID HE HOLD HIMSELF?

_____

_____

_____

_____

_____

_____

_____

_____

DO YOU THINK YOU PICKED UP SOME OF HIS HABITS? IF SO WHICH ONES?

_____

_____

_____

_____

_____

_____

_____

FEAR & DEFENCE MECHANISMS

CAN YOU REMEMBER A TIME THAT YOUR FATHER/FATHER FIGURE TAUGHT YOU ABOUT WHAT IT MEANS TO BE A MAN/WOMAN? WHAT DID HE SAY?

_____

_____

_____

_____

_____

_____

_____

_____

_____

HOW DO YOU THINK HE HAS INFLUENCED THE WAY YOU LOVE?

_____

_____

_____

_____

_____

_____

_____

_____

FEAR & DEFENCE MECHANISMS

DID YOU EVER SEE YOUR MOTHER/MOTHER FIGURE EMBRACE VULNERABILITY? HOW DID SHE PERCEIVE IT? HOW DID SHE HOLD HERSELF?

_____

_____

_____

_____

_____

_____

_____

_____

DO YOU THINK YOU PICKED UP SOME OF HER HABITS? IF SO WHICH ONES?

_____

_____

_____

_____

_____

_____

_____

_____

FEAR & DEFENCE MECHANISMS

CAN YOU REMEMBER A TIME THAT YOUR MOTHER/MOTHER FIGURE TAUGHT YOU ABOUT WHAT IT MEANS TO BE A MAN/WOMAN? WHAT DID SHE SAY?

_____

_____

_____

_____

_____

_____

_____

_____

_____

HOW DO YOU THINK SHE HAS INFLUENCED THE WAY YOU LOVE?

_____

_____

_____

_____

_____

_____

_____

_____

FEAR & DEFENCE MECHANISMS

WHAT DOES VULNERABILITY MEAN TO YOU? IS IT A STRENGTH OR A WEAKNESS?

_____

_____

_____

_____

_____

_____

_____

_____

_____

WHY DO YOU SEE IT THAT WAY?

_____

_____

_____

_____

_____

_____

_____

_____

FEAR & DEFENCE MECHANISMS

DO YOU FEEL LIKE YOU CAN TRULY BE YOURSELF IN YOUR RELATIONSHIPS? DO YOU MIRROR THEIR PERSONALITY TO MAKE THEM LIKE YOU? WHY?

_____

_____

_____

_____

_____

_____

_____

_____

_____

_____

DO YOU THINK THIS MIGHT AFFECT HOW YOU CONNECT WITH SOMEONE? WHY/WHY NOT?

_____

_____

_____

_____

_____

_____

_____

FEAR & DEFENCE MECHANISMS

DO YOU USE SARCASM OR HUMOR AS A DEFENSE MECHANISM TO AVOID VULNERABILITY? DOES IT WORK?

_____

_____

_____

_____

_____

HAS ANYONE EVER CALLED YOU OUT ON THIS? IF SO, WHAT DID THEY SAY?

_____

_____

_____

_____

WHY DO YOU THINK YOU DO IT?

_____

_____

_____

_____

_____

_____

_____

FEAR & DEFENCE MECHANISMS

DO YOU SHUT DOWN WHEN YOU FEEL LIKE YOU NEED TO PROTECT YOURSELF EMOTIONALLY?

_____

_____

_____

_____

_____

_____

_____

_____

_____

_____

WHAT'S YOUR GO-TO MOVE TO EMOTIONALLY SHUT DOWN.

_____

_____

_____

_____

_____

_____

FEAR & DEFENCE MECHANISMS

DO YOU PUSH FRIENDS OR FAMILY AWAY? DO YOU HIDE PARTS OF YOURSELF FROM THESE PEOPLE? IF SO, WHAT PARTS?

_____

_____

_____

_____

_____

_____

_____

_____

_____

WHY DO YOU DO THIS? WHAT ARE YOU HIDING?

_____

_____

_____

_____

_____

_____

_____

FEAR & DEFENCE MECHANISMS

CAN YOU RECALL A SITUATION IN A RELATIONSHIP WHERE YOU FELT LIKE YOU HAD TO CONTROL EVERYTHING?

HOW DID IT AFFECT THE DYNAMICS OF THE RELATIONSHIP?

WHAT WOULD YOU DO DIFFERENTLY NOW?

FEAR & DEFENCE MECHANISMS

WHAT'S SOMETHING YOU WISH YOU SAID TO SOMEONE THAT YOU HAVEN'T YET? WRITE IT DOWN.

_____

_____

_____

_____

_____

_____

_____

_____

WHY HAVEN'T YOU SAID IT?

_____

_____

_____

_____

_____

_____

_____

FEAR & DEFENCE MECHANISMS

WHEN WAS THE LAST TIME YOU CRIED? WHAT HAPPENED? EXPLAIN IN DETAIL.

_____

_____

_____

_____

_____

_____

_____

_____

_____

_____

DID IT FEEL CATHARTIC OR DID YOU FEEL SHAME AFTERWARD? WHY?

_____

_____

_____

_____

_____

_____

_____

FEAR & DEFENCE MECHANISMS

WHEN WAS THE LAST TIME YOU CRIED <u>IN FRONT OF SOMEONE?</u> WHAT HAPPENED?

_____

_____

_____

_____

_____

_____

_____

_____

HOW DID THAT MAKE YOU FEEL? DID YOU FEEL SUPPORTED OR REGRET IT?

_____

_____

_____

_____

_____

_____

_____

_____

FEAR & DEFENCE MECHANISMS

REFLECT ON A MOMENT WHEN YOU FELT A SURGE OF IRRATIONAL FEAR IN A RELATIONSHIP.

_____

_____

_____

_____

_____

_____

_____

_____

_____

WHAT DEFENSE MECHANISMS KICKED IN?

_____

_____

_____

_____

_____

_____

_____

_____

FEAR & DEFENCE MECHANISMS

DRAW LINES OUT FROM "MY CIRCLE" OF EVERY PERSON IN YOUR LIFE THAT YOU TRUST RIGHT NOW.

My Circle

FEAR & DEFENCE MECHANISMS

WHY DO YOU TRUST THESE PEOPLE? WHO DIDN'T MAKE THE CUT AND WHY?

FEAR & DEFENCE MECHANISMS

CAN YOU IDENTIFY ANY SELF-SABOTAGING BEHAVIORS IN YOUR RELATIONSHIPS? WHAT ARE YOUR TACTICS?

_____

_____

_____

_____

_____

HOW DO THESE BEHAVIORS SERVE YOU, AND WHAT MIGHT THEY BE PROTECTING YOU FROM?

_____

_____

_____

_____

_____

HOW DO THESE BEHAVIORS LIMIT YOU AND HOLD YOU BACK FROM DEEP CONNECTION?

_____

_____

_____

FEAR & DEFENCE MECHANISMS

ON A SCALE OF 1 TO 10, HOW COMFORTABLE DO YOU FEEL WHEN
YOU'RE ALONE? HOW ABOUT WHEN YOU'RE IN A GROUP?

ALONE

(1) (2) (3) (4) (5) (6) (7) (8) (9) (10)

IN A GROUP

(1) (2) (3) (4) (5) (6) (7) (8) (9) (10)

IS THERE A DIFFERENCE? IF SO, WHY?

_____

_____

_____

_____

_____

_____

_____

_____

_____

_____

FEAR & DEFENCE MECHANISMS

WHAT'S THE ANGRIEST YOU'VE EVER BEEN? WHAT HAPPENED? HOW DID YOU REACT?

_____

_____

_____

_____

_____

_____

_____

WAS YOUR REACTION VALID?

_____

_____

_____

_____

_____

_____

_____

WHAT WOULD YOU HAVE DONE DIFFERENTLY NOW?

_____

_____

_____

_____

FEAR & DEFENCE MECHANISMS

DO YOU TEND TO KEEP YOUR PERSONAL LIFE AND FEELINGS PRIVATE, EVEN FROM THOSE CLOSE TO YOU? WHY DO YOU THINK THIS IS?

_____

_____

_____

_____

_____

_____

WHO IS SOMEONE THAT YOU HAVE COMFORTABLY OPENED UP TO? WHY DID YOU CHOOSE THEM?

_____

_____

_____

_____

_____

HOW DOES OPENING UP TO THIS PERSON MAKE YOU FEEL?

_____

_____

_____

_____

FEAR & DEFENCE MECHANISMS

DO YOU HAVE ANYTHING THAT YOU WOULD CONSIDER AN ADDICTION? IF SO WHAT IS IT?

_____

_____

_____

_____

WHAT TRIGGERS YOU TO ENGAGE IN IT?

_____

_____

_____

_____

HOW DO YOU THINK THIS COPING MECHANISM SERVES YOU?

_____

_____

_____

WHAT FEELINGS, FEARS OR INSECURITIES DO YOU THINK YOU'RE MASKING?

_____

_____

_____

_____

FEAR & DEFENCE MECHANISMS

CAN YOU RECALL A TIME WHEN YOU PREFERRED TO SOLVE A PROBLEM
BY YOURSELF, EVEN WHEN OTHERS OFFERED HELP? WHAT LED YOU TO
THAT CHOICE?

_____

_____

_____

_____

_____

_____

_____

HOW DOES ACCOMPLISHING THINGS ALONE MAKE YOU FEEL?

_____

_____

_____

_____

HOW DOES ACCOMPLISHING THINGS WITH SOMEONE ELSE MAKE YOU
FEEL?

_____

_____

_____

_____

FEAR & DEFENCE MECHANISMS

HOW OFTEN DO YOU MAKE DECISIONS BASED PURELY ON LOGIC, IGNORING YOUR EMOTIONAL RESPONSE?

_____
_____
_____
_____
_____
_____
_____
_____

WHAT'S THE REASONING BEHIND THIS APPROACH?

_____
_____
_____
_____
_____
_____
_____

FEAR & DEFENCE MECHANISMS

HAS A PAST LOVE INTEREST EVER MADE YOU FEEL INSECURE ABOUT THEIR COMMITMENT TO YOU? WHO WAS IT AND WHAT DID THEY DO?

_____

_____

_____

_____

_____

_____

_____

_____

_____

DID YOU LOSE YOUR TRUST FOR THEM? HOW DO YOU THINK THIS IMPACTS YOU STILL?

_____

_____

_____

_____

_____

_____

_____

_____

FEAR & DEFENCE MECHANISMS

WHAT IS THE BIGGEST LIE YOU TELL ABOUT YOURSELF TO YOUR CLOSEST FRIENDS?

_____

_____

_____

_____

_____

_____

_____

_____

WHAT TRUTH ARE YOU TRYING TO AVOID?

_____

_____

_____

_____

_____

_____

_____

FEAR & DEFENCE MECHANISMS

LIST THREE FEARS THAT YOU'D
LIKE TO OVERCOME.

_____

_____

_____

_____

_____

_____

_____

_____

_____

WHAT STEPS COULD YOU TAKE TO CONQUER THEM?

_____

_____

_____

_____

_____

_____

_____

_____

FEAR & DEFENCE MECHANISMS

HAVE YOU EVER AVOIDED MAKING PLANS FOR THE FUTURE? WHAT HAPPENS INSIDE OF YOUR HEAD WHEN YOU THINK TOO FAR FORWARD?

_____

_____

_____

_____

_____

_____

_____

_____

_____

DOES THIS ONLY APPLY IN ROMANTIC RELATIONSHIPS OR DOES THIS AFFECT EVERYTHING YOU DO?

_____

_____

_____

_____

_____

_____

_____

_____

FEAR & DEFENCE MECHANISMS

WHEN WAS THE LAST TIME THAT YOU TRULY STRUGGLED? WHAT WAS HAPPENING IN YOUR LIFE? DESCRIBE IT IN DETAIL.

_____

_____

_____

_____

_____

_____

_____

_____

_____

DID YOU TURN TO ANYONE OR DID YOU ISOLATE? WHY? HOW DID THAT MAKE YOU FEEL?

_____

_____

_____

_____

_____

_____

_____

_____

FEAR & DEFENCE MECHANISMS

RECALL A MOMENT WHEN YOUR DEFENSE MECHANISMS FAILED YOU, EXPOSING YOUR VULNERABILITIES.

_____

_____

_____

_____

_____

_____

_____

_____

_____

HOW DID YOU HANDLE THAT SITUATION?

_____

_____

_____

_____

_____

_____

_____

_____

FEAR & DEFENCE MECHANISMS

CONSIDER THE FEARS YOU HAVE ABOUT BEING TRULY SEEN OR UNDERSTOOD. WHAT DO YOU TRULY FEAR? THINK ABOUT IT.

_____

_____

_____

_____

_____

_____

_____

_____

_____

HOW DO THESE FEARS SHAPE YOUR INTERACTIONS WITH OTHERS?

_____

_____

_____

_____

_____

_____

_____

_____

FEAR & DEFENCE MECHANISMS

REFLECT ON A TIME WHEN YOUR DEFENSE MECHANISMS DID MORE HARM THAN GOOD.

_____

_____

_____

_____

_____

_____

_____

_____

_____

WHAT LESSONS DID YOU DRAW FROM THIS?

_____

_____

_____

_____

_____

_____

_____

_____

FEAR & DEFENCE MECHANISMS

WHAT'S SOMETHING YOU WANT TO SAY TO YOUR FATHER/FATHER FIGURE AS THE PERSON YOU ARE NOW, EVEN IF YOU NEVER GET TO SAY IT. WRITE IT OUT, DON'T HOLD BACK.

FEAR & DEFENCE MECHANISMS

**WHAT'S SOMETHING YOU WANT TO SAY TO YOUR
MOTHER/MOTHER FIGURE AS THE PERSON YOU ARE NOW, EVEN
IF YOU NEVER GET TO SAY IT. WRITE IT OUT, DON'T HOLD BACK.**

FEAR & DEFENCE MECHANISMS

WHAT'S SOMETHING YOU REALLY NEED TO CONSCIOUSLY GET OVER?

_____

_____

_____

_____

_____

_____

_____

_____

_____

HOW CAN YOU FORGIVE YOURSELF FOR HOLDING ONTO THIS FOR TOO LONG?

_____

_____

_____

_____

_____

_____

_____

_____

RELATIONSHIPS, SEX & INTIMACY

RELATIONSHIPS, SEX & INTIMACY

REFLECT ON A TIME WHEN YOU WERE DRAWN TO SOMEONE WHO
WASN'T THE BEST CHOICE FOR YOU. WHO WERE THEY AND WHAT
DREW YOU TO THEM?

_____

_____

_____

_____

_____

_____

_____

_____

_____

DO YOU LOOK AT THEM DIFFERENTLY NOW?

_____

_____

_____

_____

_____

_____

_____

RELATIONSHIPS, SEX & INTIMACY

IF YOU HAD THE CHANCE TO REVISIT A PAST RELATIONSHIP AND CHANGE ONE THING, WHAT WOULD IT BE?

_____

_____

_____

_____

_____

_____

_____

_____

CAN YOU FORGIVE YOURSELF?

_____

_____

_____

_____

_____

_____

_____

RELATIONSHIPS, SEX & INTIMACY

DESCRIBE A TIME WHEN YOU WERE SIMULTANEOUSLY ATTRACTED TO SOMEONE BUT PUSHED THEM AWAY. WHAT HAPPENED?

_____

_____

_____

_____

_____

_____

DID YOU SELF SABOTAGE? IF SO, HOW AND WHY?

_____

_____

_____

_____

_____

WOULD YOU REACT DIFFERENTLY NOW?

_____

_____

_____

_____

RELATIONSHIPS, SEX & INTIMACY

HAVE YOU EVER BEEN CHEATED ON OR TREATED POORLY IN A RELATIONSHIP? WHAT HAPPENED?

_____

_____

_____

_____

_____

_____

WHY DO YOU THINK THIS HAPPENED? HOW DID IT CHANGE THE WAY YOU VIEW RELATIONSHIPS?

_____

_____

_____

_____

_____

DO YOU THINK THIS STILL AFFECTS YOU? HOW CAN YOU LET GO?

_____

_____

_____

_____

_____

RELATIONSHIPS, SEX & INTIMACY

REFLECT ON A SITUATION WHERE YOU FELT DEEPLY HURT OR BETRAYED IN A RELATIONSHIP. WHAT HAPPENED AND HOW DID IT PLAY OUT?

_____

_____

_____

_____

_____

_____

_____

_____

_____

_____

HOW DO YOU DESERVE TO BE TREATED?

_____

_____

_____

_____

_____

_____

_____

_____

_____

RELATIONSHIPS, SEX & INTIMACY

CAN YOU FORIGIVE YOUR EX? WHY/ WHY NOT?

_____

_____

_____

_____

_____

_____

_____

_____

CAN YOU FORGIVE YOURSELF FOR HOLDING ONTO THEM?

_____

_____

_____

_____

_____

_____

_____

_____

RELATIONSHIPS, SEX & INTIMACY

DO YOU THINK YOU'VE EVER ACTUALLY BEEN IN LOVE? IF SO, WITH WHO AND HOW DID IT FEEL? IF NOT, WHY NOT?

_____

_____

_____

_____

_____

_____

_____

_____

_____

_____

WHAT DOES BEING IN LOVE LOOK LIKE TO YOU?

_____

_____

_____

_____

_____

_____

_____

_____

_____

_____

RELATIONSHIPS, SEX & INTIMACY

WHAT'S THE WORST THING YOU'VE DONE TO SOMEONE IN A RELATIONSHIP?

_____

_____

_____

_____

_____

_____

_____

_____

_____

WHAT WOULD YOUR HONEST REACTION HAVE BEEN IF SOMONE DID THAT TO YOU?

_____

_____

_____

_____

_____

_____

_____

_____

RELATIONSHIPS, SEX & INTIMACY

WHY DO YOU PUSH PEOPLE AWAY WHEN THEY START TO GET CLOSE? WRITE ABOUT A SPECIFIC TIME THAT YOU DID IT AND HOW YOU JUSTIFIED IT.

_____

_____

_____

_____

_____

_____

_____

_____

_____

WHAT DO YOU THINK TRIGGERS YOU?

_____

_____

_____

_____

_____

_____

_____

RELATIONSHIPS, SEX & INTIMACY

REMEMBER A TIME IN A RELATIONSHIP WHEN YOU FELT AN OVERWHELMING NEED TO ESCAPE OR CREATE DISTANCE. WHAT HAPPENED? WHAT DID YOU DO?

_____

_____

_____

_____

_____

_____

_____

_____

WHAT WERE YOU FEELING AT THAT MOMENT?

_____

_____

_____

_____

_____

_____

_____

_____

RELATIONSHIPS, SEX & INTIMACY

WHAT WAS YOUR GREATEST HEARTBREAK? WHO WAS IT WITH? HOW DID IT END?

_____

_____

_____

_____

_____

_____

_____

_____

_____

_____

WHY DID THIS ONE HIT SO HARD? WHAT DID YOU LEARN FROM IT?

_____

_____

_____

_____

_____

_____

_____

_____

RELATIONSHIPS, SEX & INTIMACY

DO YOU STRUGGLE TO RECEIVE LOVE? WHY IS IT HARD FOR YOU TO ACCEPT? WHAT HAPPENS WHEN SOMEONE NEW EXPRESSES LOVE FOR YOU?

_____

_____

_____

_____

_____

_____

_____

_____

_____

WHAT DO YOU FEEL MADE YOU THIS WAY?

_____

_____

_____

_____

_____

_____

_____

_____

RELATIONSHIPS, SEX & INTIMACY

THINKING BACK TO YOUR GREATEST HEARTBREAK, WHAT COULD YOU HAVE DONE DIFFERENTLY IN THAT RELATIONSHIP?

_____

_____

_____

_____

_____

_____

_____

WHAT'S SOMETHING YOU REGRET DOING?

_____

_____

_____

_____

_____

_____

WERE THEY GOOD FOR YOU? WHY/ WHY NOT?

_____

_____

_____

_____

RELATIONSHIPS, SEX & INTIMACY

DO YOU FEEL SHAMEFUL ABOUT ANY OF YOUR PAST EXES? IF SO, WHO WAS IT AND WHAT HAPPENED IN THE RELATIONSHIP?

_____

_____

_____

_____

_____

_____

WHAT ABOUT THE RELATIONSHIP DO YOU FEEL SHAME ABOUT?

_____

_____

_____

_____

_____

_____

HOW CAN YOU LET GO OF THIS?

_____

_____

_____

_____

RELATIONSHIPS, SEX & INTIMACY

DO YOU SUPPRESS OR HIDE YOUR OWN EMOTIONS AS A WAY TO
PROTECT YOURSELF FROM POTENTIAL REJECTION? WHY/WHY NOT?

_____

_____

_____

_____

_____

_____

WHAT COPING MECHANISMS DO YOU USE TO SUPPRESS FEELINGS FOR
SOMEONE?

_____

_____

_____

_____

_____

IS THIS HEALTHY?

_____

_____

_____

_____

RELATIONSHIPS, SEX & INTIMACY

WHAT GOES THROUGH YOUR HEAD ABOUT SOMEONE ON A FIRST DATE?
WHAT ARE YOU TRYING TO ASSESS? EXPLAIN IN DETAIL - WHAT HAPPENS
IN YOUR MIND BEFORE, DURING AND AFTER THE DATE?

RELATIONSHIPS, SEX & INTIMACY

THINK ABOUT THE LAST TIME YOU FELT INTENSE ANXIETY IN A ROMANTIC RELATIONSHIP. WHAT DID YOU DO?

_____

_____

_____

_____

_____

_____

_____

_____

_____

CAN YOU REMEMBER WHAT TRIGGERED IT?

_____

_____

_____

_____

_____

_____

_____

_____

RELATIONSHIPS, SEX & INTIMACY

HAVE THERE BEEN MOMENTS IN YOUR INTIMATE RELATIONSHIPS WHERE YOU FELT THAT YOUR EMOTIONAL NEEDS WERE NOT BEING MET? WHAT HAPPENED?

_____

_____

_____

_____

_____

_____

_____

_____

_____

HOW DO YOU COPE IN SUCH SITUATIONS?

_____

_____

_____

_____

_____

_____

_____

RELATIONSHIPS, SEX & INTIMACY

REFLECT ON YOUR FIRST SEXUAL EXPERIENCE. WHO WAS IT WITH AND HOW DID IT HAPPEN?

_____

_____

_____

_____

_____

_____

_____

_____

WHAT IMPACT HAS THIS HAD ON YOUR SEXUAL RELATIONSHIPS SINCE?

_____

_____

_____

_____

_____

_____

_____

RELATIONSHIPS, SEX & INTIMACY

EXPLORE AN EXPERIENCE WHERE YOU FELT SEXUALLY
DISCONNECTED DESPITE BEING EMOTIONALLY INVOLVED. WHO
WAS IT WITH? WHAT HAPPENED?

_____

_____

_____

_____

_____

_____

_____

_____

WHAT DO YOU THINK WAS THE UNDERLYING ISSUE?

_____

_____

_____

_____

_____

_____

_____

RELATIONSHIPS, SEX & INTIMACY

REFLECT ON A MOMENT WHEN YOU FELT THE MOST LOVED AND SECURE IN A RELATIONSHIP. WHO WAS IT WITH? HOW DID THEY TREAT YOU?

_____

_____

_____

_____

_____

_____

_____

_____

_____

CAN YOU DESCRIBE WHAT WAS HAPPENING AND HOW YOU FELT?

_____

_____

_____

_____

_____

_____

_____

_____

RELATIONSHIPS, SEX & INTIMACY

DO YOU USE CASUAL SEX AS A DISTRACTION? WHEN WAS THE LAST TIME YOU DID THIS?

_____

_____

_____

_____

_____

_____

_____

_____

HOW DO YOU FEEL IMMEDIATELY AFTER THE SEX?

_____

_____

_____

_____

_____

_____

_____

RELATIONSHIPS, SEX & INTIMACY

HOW DOES CASUAL SEX SERVE YOU?
EXPLAIN WHAT IT DOES FOR YOU.

_____

_____

_____

_____

_____

_____

_____

_____

_____

_____

HOW DOES SEX WITH AN EMOTIONAL CONNECTION DIFFER?

_____

_____

_____

_____

_____

_____

_____

_____

RELATIONSHIPS, SEX & INTIMACY

THINK ABOUT YOUR EX (WHICHEVER COMES TO MIND FIRST) WHAT WERE THINGS THAT YOU LOVED ABOUT THEM AND THINGS THAT YOU HATED?

LOVED

_____

_____

_____

_____

_____

_____

_____

_____

HATED

_____

_____

_____

_____

_____

_____

_____

_____

RELATIONSHIPS, SEX & INTIMACY

DO YOU EVER FEEL A PRESSURE TO PERFORM IN A SEXUAL SETTING? EXPLAIN WHY.

_____

_____

_____

_____

_____

_____

_____

_____

_____

WHERE DO YOU THINK THIS PRESSURE ARISES?

_____

_____

_____

_____

_____

_____

_____

_____

RELATIONSHIPS, SEX & INTIMACY

HAVE YOU EVER USED SEX AS A MEANS OF MANIPULATING THE EMOTIONAL DYNAMICS OF A RELATIONSHIP? EXPLAIN THE SITUATION.

_____

_____

_____

_____

_____

_____

_____

_____

WHY DID YOU DO IT? WHAT ENDED UP HAPPENING?

_____

_____

_____

_____

_____

_____

_____

_____

ELATIONSHIPS, SEX & INTIMACY

**HAVE YOU EVER FELT DISCONNECTED FROM YOUR
PARTNER DURING A SEXUAL ENCOUNTER?**

_____
_____
_____
_____
_____
_____
_____
_____
_____
_____

**HOW DID IT MAKE YOU FEEL, AND WHAT STEPS, IF ANY, DID YOU
TAKE TO ADDRESS IT?**

_____
_____
_____
_____
_____
_____
_____
_____
_____

RELATIONSHIPS, SEX & INTIMACY

HOW DOES SEX MAKE YOU FEEL? DO YOU ENJOY IT? DO YOU FEEL CONFIDENT? IF SO WHY, IF NOT WHY NOT?

_____

_____

_____

_____

_____

_____

_____

DO YOU EVER FEEL ANY SHAME AFTER SEX OR SELF PLEASURE? IF SO, WHY?

_____

_____

_____

_____

_____

HOW CAN YOU LET GO OF THAT SHAME?

_____

_____

_____

_____

RELATIONSHIPS, SEX & INTIMACY

DO YOU HAVE ANY FEARS OR ANXIETIES AROUND SEX? WHAT ARE THEY?

_____

_____

_____

_____

_____

_____

WHAT DO YOU THINK TRIGGERS THIS?

_____

_____

_____

_____

_____

HOW CAN YOU WORK ON THESE FEARS/ANXIETIES?

_____

_____

_____

_____

_____

_____

RELATIONSHIPS, SEX & INTIMACY

IS THERE AN EX THAT YOU FIND HARD TO LET GO? WHAT ABOUT THEM IS SO
SPECIAL TO YOU?

_____

_____

_____

_____

_____

_____

_____

_____

DO YOU THINK YOU MIGHT ROMANTICIZE THEM? HOW CAN YOU MOVE ON
FROM THEM?

_____

_____

_____

_____

_____

_____

_____

_____

RELATIONSHIPS, SEX & INTIMACY

WHAT MAKES YOU FEEL JEALOUS? WRITE EVERYTHING DOWN, EVEN IF YOU
KNOW IT FEELS WRONG - DON'T HOLD BACK

_____

_____

_____

_____

_____

_____

_____

_____

_____

_____

WHY DO YOU THINK THIS MAKES YOU FEEL JEALOUS?

_____

_____

_____

_____

_____

_____

_____

RELATIONSHIPS, SEX & INTIMACY

HOW DO YOU PERCEIVE A PARTNER'S SEXUAL DESIRES? DO YOU FEEL USED? DO YOU FEEL GOOD ABOUT SEX? DO THEY SATISFY YOU?

WHAT CAN YOU DO TO IMPROVE COMMUNICATION ABOUT THIS?

RELATIONSHIPS, SEX & INTIMACY

WHO IS SOMEONE YOU HAD AN INTENSE SEXUAL CONNECTION WITH? WAS THE EMOTIONAL CONNECTION THERE TOO? HOW DID THIS RELATIONSHIP PLAY OUT? EXPLAIN.

RELATIONSHIPS, SEX & INTIMACY

WHAT IS SOMETHING YOU HAVE DONE IN A PAST RELATIONSHIP THAT YOU KNEW WAS WRONG?

_____

_____

_____

_____

_____

_____

HOW DID YOUR PARTNER RESPOND? WHAT WAS THE RESULT?

_____

_____

_____

_____

_____

WHAT WOULD YOU DO DIFFERENTLY NOW?

_____

_____

_____

_____

RELATIONSHIPS, SEX & INTIMACY

HOW DO YOU USE DATING APPS? ARE YOU LOOKING FOR SOMETHING SERIOUS OR CASUAL? WHY?

_____

_____

_____

_____

_____

_____

DO YOU THINK YOUR RELATIONSHIP TO DATING IS HEALTHY? DOES THE WAY YOU DATE FULLFILL YOU?

_____

_____

_____

_____

_____

WHO HAS BEEN THE MOST MEMORABLE CONNECTION FROM THE APPS? WHAT HAPPENED WITH THAT PERSON?

_____

_____

_____

_____

_____

RELATIONSHIPS, SEX & INTIMACY

DO YOU HAVE FEELINGS FOR SOMEONE RIGHT NOW? WHO IS IT? WHAT DO YOU LOVE ABOUT THEM?

_____

_____

_____

_____

_____

HOW DOES IT FEEL TO BE AROUND THEM, TO TALK TO THEM?

_____

_____

_____

_____

_____

_____

WHY HAVEN'T YOU TOLD THEM?

_____

_____

_____

RELATIONSHIPS, SEX & INTIMACY

IF YOU CURRENTLY HAVE A PARTNER WRITE DOWN EVERYTHING YOU
APPRECIATE ABOUT THEM.

_____

_____

_____

_____

_____

_____

_____

_____

_____

NOW OPEN UP ABOUT THINGS YOU'D LIKE TO WORK ON IN THE
RELATIONSHIP.

_____

_____

_____

_____

_____

_____

_____

RELATIONSHIPS, SEX & INTIMACY

WHAT SACRIFICES DID YOU MAKE IN YOUR MOST SIGNIFICANT RELATIONSHIP?

_____

_____

_____

_____

_____

_____

DID YOU FEEL APPRECIATED?

_____

_____

_____

_____

_____

_____

HOW DID THIS RELATIONSHIP SHAPE THE WAY YOU SEE YOUR FUTURE RELATIONSHIPS?

_____

_____

_____

_____

RELATIONSHIPS, SEX & INTIMACY

DESCRIBE YOUR BEST SEXUAL EXPERIENCE IN DETAIL. WHO WAS IT WITH, WHERE WERE YOU, WHAT DID YOU DO, HOW DID IT FEEL? WRITE THE STORY.

RELATIONSHIPS, SEX & INTIMACY

DESCRIBE MOMENTS OF DEEP LONELINESS. WHAT HAPPENS INSIDE YOUR
HEAD? HOW DO YOU COPE? WRITE OUT WHAT YOU DO.

RELATIONSHIPS, SEX & INTIMACY

WRITE DOWN EVERYTHING YOU LOVED AND EVERYTHING YOU HATED
ABOUT YOUR EX. DON'T BE SHY.

LOVED

_____

_____

_____

_____

_____

_____

_____

HATED

_____

_____

_____

_____

_____

_____

_____

_____

RELATIONSHIPS, SEX & INTIMACY

WRITE A LETTER TO AN EX THAT HURT YOU - SAY EXACTLY HOW YOU FEEL WITHOUT HOLDING ANYTHING BACK.

_____

_____

_____

_____

_____

_____

_____

_____

_____

_____

_____

_____

_____

_____

_____

_____

_____

_____

_____

_____

_____

RELATIONSHIPS, SEX & INTIMACY

DESCRIBE THE WAYS YOU MAY AVOID OR SABOTAGE OPPORTUNITIES FOR DEEP CONNECTION AND INTIMACY.

_____

_____

_____

_____

_____

_____

_____

_____

_____

ARE YOU GETTING SICK AND TIRED OF THIS PATTERN? WHY/WHY NOT?

_____

_____

_____

_____

_____

_____

RELATIONSHIPS, SEX & INTIMACY

HOW COMFORTABLE DO YOU FEEL EXPRESSING YOUR SEXUAL FANTASIES?

_____

_____

_____

_____

_____

_____

_____

_____

_____

WHAT ARE THEY?

_____

_____

_____

_____

_____

_____

RELATIONSHIPS, SEX & INTIMACY

HOW DOES YOUR MINDSET CHANGE WHEN YOU TRANSITION FROM CASUAL INTIMACY TO SEXUAL INTIMACY IN A RELATIONSHIP?

_____

_____

_____

_____

_____

_____

_____

_____

_____

_____

WHAT HAPPENS TO YOUR THOUGHTS? ARE YOU THINKING ABOUT THEM OBSESSIVELY AFTERWARD? OR PUSHING THOUGHTS AWAY?

_____

_____

_____

_____

_____

_____

_____

RELATIONSHIPS, SEX & INTIMACY

DESCRIBE HOW YOU FEEL WHEN A SEXUAL EXPERIENCE DOES NOT MEET YOUR EXPECTATIONS. WHEN WAS THE LAST TIME THIS HAPPENED AND WHO WAS IT WITH? EXPLAIN.

_____

_____

_____

_____

_____

_____

_____

_____

_____

_____

HOW DID YOU REACT?

_____

_____

_____

_____

_____

_____

_____

RELATIONSHIPS, SEX & INTIMACY

DESCRIBE A TIME WHEN YOUR EMOTIONS DURING OR AFTER SEX WERE A SURPRISE TO YOU.

_____

_____

_____

_____

_____

_____

_____

_____

_____

_____

WHAT DID YOU LEARN FROM THIS EXPERIENCE?

_____

_____

_____

_____

_____

_____

_____

RELATIONSHIPS, SEX & INTIMACY

HOW WOULD YOU LIKE YOUR SEX LIFE TO LOOK IN THE FUTURE? WRITE A
DETAILED SCENARIO FROM EMOTIONAL INTIMACY TO FOREPLAY, SEX AND
AFTER CARE.

_____

_____

_____

_____

_____

_____

_____

_____

_____

_____

_____

_____

_____

_____

_____

_____

_____

_____

_____

_____

_____

_____

RELATIONSHIPS, SEX & INTIMACY

HOW COMFORTABLE ARE YOU WITH EXPRESSING VULNERABILITY IN YOUR RELATIONSHIPS? THINK ABOUT A MOMENT WHEN YOU FELT PARTICULARLY VULNERABLE.

_____

_____

_____

_____

_____

_____

_____

_____

_____

HOW DID IT FEEL TO OPEN UP?

_____

_____

_____

_____

_____

_____

_____

_____

RELATIONSHIPS, SEX & INTIMACY

HOW DO YOU COMMUNICATE YOUR NEEDS AND DESIRES WHEN IT COMES TO SEX?

_____

_____

_____

_____

_____

_____

_____

_____

_____

DO YOU FIND THIS EASY OR CHALLENGING?

_____

_____

_____

_____

_____

_____

RELATIONSHIPS, SEX & INTIMACY

WRITE A FORGIVENESS LETTER TO YOURSELF FOR ANY PAST
MISTAKES OR REGRETS IN RELATIONSHIPS. BE AS HONEST AS
YOU CAN.

ENVISIONING THE FUTURE

ENVISIONING THE FUTURE

The Importance of Visualization

Congrats on making it this far!

You've done a whole lot of work, **probably cried a little** and figured some things out about yourself that **you didn't even realize.**

Now we start getting to the fun stuff.

Who do you **want** to become? What does your **glow up era look like?**

And why does **visualization matter?**

We've already **learnt some cool stuff about the subconscious mind** and now we'll take it a step further.

A significant part of the subconscious mind's power lies in the **Reticular Activating System (RAS).**

Your RAS is a **network of neurons** located in the brainstem that plays a critical role in controlling wakefulness and focus.

You don't realize it but your brain is taking in **a ton of information everyday.**

Your brain can't possibly **store all of this information.**

So, your RAS acts as a filter, deciding **what information should be given attention and what to overlook.**

When you **visualize a desired future,** your RAS **becomes attuned to opportunities, information, and experiences aligned with that future.**

Just like that weird feeling when you **learn a new word** and then all of a sudden you start hearing it everywhere, your RAS will **tune into what you have laid out for your future plans and show you messaging to encourage action.**

ENVISIONING THE FUTURE

The Importance of Visualization

Before you start envisioning your future in the next set of prompts, we want to give you some **pointers for visualization.**

Remember that:

1. Thoughts are the language of the brain:

- Our brains respond to our **thoughts and beliefs**, whether they're about our current reality or an imagined future. **Your thoughts and beliefs become your reality.**

2. Feelings are the language of the body:

- Our body responds to our **feelings**, which are often the product of our thoughts. If we can feel the emotions of our desired future <u>now</u>, our **body can be 'tricked' into thinking that future is already our reality, resulting in more positive thoughts and telling your brain's RAS to focus on positive outcomes.**

3. The alignment of thoughts and feelings creates a state of being:

- When our thoughts **(brain) and feelings (body) align,** we enter a state of being. This state can **influence our actions, choices, and experiences, which ultimately shapes our reality.**

4. Mental rehearsal is key:

- Just as athletes mentally rehearse their performances, **we can mentally rehearse our desired future.** This process, done regularly, can **build neural pathways** in our brain that supports that future.

ENVISIONING THE FUTURE

How to Visualize

Here's how to apply these teachings through visualization while doing shadow work:

1. Create a Clear Mental Picture:

- Define **what your future looks like** in detail. What are you doing? Who are you with? How do you feel?

2. Feel the Future Now:

- **Engage your emotions as you visualize.** Feel the joy, excitement, love, or peace of your future now. This convinces your body that this future is happening now.

3. Mental Rehearsal:

- Regularly visualize your future, **immersing yourself in the feelings it brings**. This practice, done over time, reinforces the neural pathways that align with this future.

4. Let Go:

- **Detach from the outcome and trust the process.** Don't stress about how or when your desired future will manifest. Your job is to **create it mentally and emotionally, and then let it unfold naturally.**

5. Take Aligned Action:

- **Visualization isn't a replacement for action;** it's a **catalyst**. Inspired ideas or opportunities may come to you – **act on them.** They're part of the path to your **visualized future.**

ENVISIONING THE FUTURE

REMEMBER THE WEB OF BELIEFS YOU DREW AT THE START OF YOUR JOURNEY?
HAVE YOUR BELIEFS CHANGED? WHAT ARE YOUR NEW BELIEFS?

My Beliefs

ENVISIONING THE FUTURE

HAVE YOU BEEN PRACTICING REDIRECTING THOSE NEGATIVE THOUGHTS? IF SO, DO YOU NOTICE ANY CHANGES? WHAT ARE THEY? IF NOT, NAUGHTY.

_____

_____

_____

_____

_____

_____

WHAT THOUGHTS HAVE YOU CAUGHT THIS WEEK? WHAT'S BEEN ON YOUR MIND?

_____

_____

_____

_____

_____

_____

_____

_____

_____

_____

ENVISIONING THE FUTURE

HOW HAS BEING ABLE TO NOTICE YOUR SUBCONSCIOUS THOUGHTS FELT?
DO YOU NOTICE IT MORE?

ENVISIONING THE FUTURE

WHERE DO YOU WANT TO TRAVEL IN THE NEXT 5 YEARS? WRITE ABOUT
WHERE YOU WANT TO GO IN DETAIL AND WHAT YOU'LL DO THERE.

ENVISIONING THE FUTURE

DRAW A "VISION BOARD" WITH IMAGES AND WORDS THAT REPRESENT WHAT
YOU WANT IN YOUR FUTURE.

ENVISIONING THE FUTURE

ENVISION YOUR FUTURE HOUSE/S IN VIVID DETAIL. WHERE IS IT, WHAT
DOES IT LOOK LIKE, WHO'S WITH YOU?

_____

_____

_____

_____

_____

_____

_____

_____

_____

_____

_____

_____

_____

_____

_____

_____

_____

_____

_____

ENVISIONING THE FUTURE

ENVISION YOUR FUTURE CAR/S, WHAT ARE YOU DRIVING? HOW DOES IT FEEL TO HAVE YOUR DREAM CAR? WHERE ARE YOU GOING IN IT?

_____

_____

_____

_____

_____

_____

_____

_____

_____

_____

_____

_____

_____

_____

_____

_____

_____

ENVISIONING THE FUTURE

RECORD A MESSAGE TO YOUR FUTURE SELF ON YOUR PHONE ABOUT YOUR HOPES AND DREAMS. PUT AN ALARM IN YOUR PHONE TO REMIND YOU TO LISTEN TO IT 6 MONTHS FROM NOW. WHAT DID YOU SAY?

ENVISIONING THE FUTURE

REFLECT ON THE PERSONAL GROWTH YOU'D LIKE TO SEE IN YOURSELF A YEAR FROM NOW.

_____

_____

_____

_____

_____

_____

_____

_____

_____

WHAT EMOTIONAL OR MENTAL SHIFTS ARE YOU AIMING FOR?

_____

_____

_____

_____

_____

_____

_____

_____

ENVISIONING THE FUTURE

DRAW LINES OUT FROM "PERFECT PERSON" OF ALL THE QUALITIES YOU WANT IN A PARTNER.

Perfect Person

ENVISIONING THE FUTURE

IMAGINE YOUR PERFECT PERSON. WRITE A LIST OF PHYSICAL AND
EMOTIONAL QUALITIES THIS PERSON HAS

PHYSICAL

_____

_____

_____

_____

_____

_____

_____

_____

EMOTIONAL

_____

_____

_____

_____

_____

_____

_____

ENVISIONING THE FUTURE

HOW DOES THIS FUTURE PARTNER:

SUPPORT YOU

_____

_____

_____

_____

_____

_____

_____

LOVE YOU

_____

_____

_____

_____

_____

_____

_____

_____

ENVISIONING THE FUTURE

WRITE ABOUT WHAT YOUR BIGGEST PASSIONS AND INTERESTS.

_____
_____
_____
_____
_____
_____
_____
_____
_____

DOES YOUR PARTNER/FUTURE PARTNER NEED TO SHARE THESE INTERESTS.
IF SO, WHICH ONES?

_____
_____
_____
_____
_____
_____
_____
_____

ENVISIONING THE FUTURE

WHAT'S THEIR PERSONALITY LIKE? HOW DO YOU HANG OUT? WHAT DOES IT LOOK LIKE AT HOME TOGETHER?

ENVISIONING THE FUTURE

HOW DOES YOUR IDEAL PARTNER TREAT YOU? EXPLAIN IN DETAIL.

_____

_____

_____

_____

_____

_____

_____

_____

HOW DO YOU SHOW YOUR IDEAL PARTNER LOVE AND SUPPORT? EXPLAIN IN DETAIL.

_____

_____

_____

_____

_____

_____

_____

_____

ENVISIONING THE FUTURE

DRAW A CIRCLE WITH YOUR NAME IN THE CENTRE. WRITE EVERYTHING THAT IS GOING TO BE IMPORTANT TO YOU IN THE NEXT YEAR OF YOUR LIFE.

ENVISIONING THE FUTURE

CREATE A BUCKET LIST FOR THE NEXT FIVE YEARS. WHAT ADVENTURES
ARE ON THERE?

_____

_____

_____

_____

_____

_____

_____

_____

_____

_____

_____

_____

_____

_____

_____

_____

_____

_____

_____

_____

_____

ENVISIONING THE FUTURE

PICTURE A TYPICAL FRIDAY NIGHT ONE YEAR FROM NOW. WHAT ARE YOU DOING? WHO ARE YOU WITH? WHAT'S MAKING YOU SMILE?

ENVISIONING THE FUTURE

CLOSE YOUR EYES AND IMAGINE A MOMENT WHERE YOU EXPERIENCE PURE EMOTIONAL PEACE. WHAT DOES THIS MOMENT LOOK LIKE, AND HOW DOES YOUR BODY FEEL? WHERE ARE YOU? WHAT ARE YOU DOING? WHO IS WITH YOU?

ENVISIONING THE FUTURE

CREATE A PLAYLIST FOR A FUTURE ROAD TRIP. WHERE ARE YOU GOING
AND WHAT SIGHTS ARE YOU SEEING? PLAY IT AS YOU'RE WRITING.

ENVISIONING THE FUTURE

PICTURE YOUR FUTURE SELF IN PERFECT HEALTH. HOW DOES YOUR BODY FEEL? WHAT ACTIVITIES ARE YOU ABLE TO DO WITH EASE?

_____

_____

_____

_____

_____

_____

_____

_____

_____

WHAT STEPS CAN YOU TAKE THIS WEEK TO GET THERE?

_____

_____

_____

_____

_____

_____

_____

ENVISIONING THE FUTURE

IF YOU HAD NO FEAR OR LIMITATIONS, WHAT WOULD YOUR LIFE LOOK LIKE IN 5 YEARS?

ENVISIONING THE FUTURE

PLAN AN ITINERARY FOR A WEEKEND GETAWAY IN YOUR FUTURE. WHERE ARE YOU GOING, AND WHAT ACTIVITIES ARE YOU DOING?

_____

_____

_____

_____

_____

_____

_____

_____

_____

WHAT STEPS CAN YOU TAKE TO MAKE THIS TRIP A REALITY?

_____

_____

_____

_____

_____

_____

ENVISIONING THE FUTURE

CREATE A MENTAL IMAGE OF YOURSELF PRACTICING DAILY RITUALS THAT
NURTURE YOUR WELL-BEING. WHAT ARE THEY? HOW DO THESE RITUALS
CONTRIBUTE TO YOUR EMOTIONAL STABILITY?

_____

_____

_____

_____

_____

_____

_____

_____

WHEN ARE YOU GOING TO GET STARTED?

_____

_____

_____

_____

_____

_____

ENVISIONING THE FUTURE

WRITE A LETTER TO YOUR FUTURE SELF FIVE YEARS FROM NOW. WHAT DO
YOU HOPE TO HAVE ACHIEVED?

ENVISIONING THE FUTURE

WHAT DOES FINANCIAL FREEDOM LOOK LIKE TO YOU? IF YOU HAD
EVERYTHING YOU DESIRED WHAT DOES YOUR LIFE LOOK LIKE? EXPLAIN IN
VIVID DETAIL.

ENVISIONING THE FUTURE

VISUALIZE A DAY WHEN YOU FEEL TRULY CONTENT. WHAT HAS
HAPPENED TO MAKE YOU FEEL THIS WAY? WRITE ABOUT YOUR DAY
FROM WAKING UP TO GOING TO SLEEP IN DETAIL.

ENVISIONING THE FUTURE

WHAT'S A SKILL YOU'D LOVE TO MASTER IN THE FUTURE?

_____

_____

_____

_____

_____

_____

_____

_____

_____

_____

WHAT ARE SOME STEPS YOU CAN TAKE TO ACHIEVE THIS NOW?

_____

_____

_____

_____

_____

ENVISIONING THE FUTURE

**ENVISION THE ULTIMATE VERSION OF YOUR LIFE. WHAT HAVE YOU LET
GO OF? WHAT HAVE YOU GAINED?**

_____

_____

_____

_____

_____

_____

_____

_____

_____

_____

_____

_____

_____

_____

_____

_____

_____

_____

_____

_____

_____

ENVISIONING THE FUTURE

WRITE A LETTER FROM YOUR FUTURE SELF FORGIVING YOUR PAST
SELF FOR ANY PERCEIVED MISTAKES OR FAILURES - NAME THEM.

HOW DOES FORGIVING YOURSELF FEEL?

ENVISIONING THE FUTURE

WRITE A FUTURE DIARY ENTRY AFTER YOU'VE ACHIEVED A SIGNIFICANT
GOAL. WHAT WAS THE GOAL? HOW DID YOU ACHIEVE IT? WHAT
EMOTIONS ARE YOU FEELING?

ENVISIONING THE FUTURE

THINK OF A POSITIVE OUTCOME YOU DESIRE. WHAT IS IT? HOW WOULD
ACHIEVING IT MAKE YOU FEEL? SPEND SOME TIME EACH DAY FEELING THAT
EMOTION INTENSELY, AS IF YOUR DESIRE HAS ALREADY MANIFESTED.

_____

_____

_____

_____

_____

_____

_____

_____

_____

_____

WHAT STEPS CAN YOU TAKE TO MAKE THIS A REALITY?

_____

_____

_____

_____

_____

_____

ENVISIONING THE FUTURE

IDENTIFY ONE MAJOR RELATIONSHIP GOAL YOU'D LIKE TO REACH
WITHIN THE NEXT SIX MONTHS.

_____

_____

_____

_____

_____

_____

_____

_____

_____

WHAT CONCRETE ACTIONS WILL HELP YOU GET THERE?

_____

_____

_____

_____

_____

_____

_____

ENVISIONING THE FUTURE

**LOOK BACK AT THE PERSON YOU WERE WHEN YOU STARTED THIS
JOURNAL AND COMPARE IT WITH THE PERSON YOU ARE NOW. WHAT
HAVE YOU LEARNED?**

_____

_____

_____

_____

_____

_____

_____

_____

_____

_____

_____

_____

**IN WHAT WAYS HAVE YOU GROWN AND CHANGED? WHAT ARE YOU MOST
PROUD OF?**

_____

_____

_____

_____

_____

_____

ENVISIONING THE FUTURE

CREATE AN ACTION PLAN FOR THE NEXT SIX MONTHS BASED ON YOUR
VISIONS. BREAK IT DOWN INTO STEPS. START SMALL AND BUILD.

_____

_____

_____

_____

_____

_____

_____

_____

_____

_____

_____

_____

_____

_____

_____

_____

_____

_____

_____

ENVISIONING THE FUTURE

ENVISIONING THE FUTURE

_____

_____

_____

_____

_____

_____

_____

_____

_____

_____

_____

_____

_____

_____

_____

_____

_____

_____

_____

AFFIRMATIONS

AFFIRMATIONS FOR BREAKING DISORGANIZED PATTERNS

Look at you go! The hard part is done and **you've done awesome!**

You've probably **learnt a lot about yourself, maybe had a few cries and crazy realizations,** now we're going to lock in all of this progress with positive affirmations.

Using positive affirmations is a powerful way to **influence your subconscious mind.**

Remember, you think around **90% of the same subconscious thoughts everyday.**

You now have a **vision for the future**, but it's also important to keep your thoughts **focused and positive.**

Remember, this isn't a 100% of the time thing.

You're allowed to have bad days - and when you do take that time to rest, be upset, be angry, eat the junk food - feel everything you need to feel.

Then - get back to it.

When you repeat positive affirmations you're feeding the brain new information and **creating new neural pathways** that will help you to shift your programming.

Remember it **takes 30 days to create new neural pathways.**

It's important to acknowledge that affirmations **may feel a bit strange or awkward** at first.

Talking to yourself in a **positive and empowering way** might not be something you're used to, but trust us when we say they can be incredibly transformative.

Affirmations are like little **seeds that we plant in our minds**. With consistent practice, they have the power to **reprogram our thoughts and beliefs**, helping us break free from disorganized patterns and embrace healthier ways of relating to ourselves and others.

So, even if **it feels a bit weird or corny, give affirmations a chance.**

Repeat them to yourself with **conviction and intention**. Over time, you'll begin to notice a shift in your mindset and a **greater sense of self-worth and self-acceptance.**

AFFIRMATIONS FOR BREAKING DISORGANIZED PATTERNS

Tips For Affirmations

You can practice your disorganized attachment style affirmations either **inside your head or out loud.**

Practicing in a **quiet space when you have a little time to yourself** is best, so that you can focus on the words and emotion.

You can choose to **practice in the mirror** while looking into your eyes to enhance the practice.

Remember, we need to connect the thoughts of the mind to a feeling in the body, so **attach a deep feeling to your affirmation.**

- Don't just say the words **"I deserve love"**, feel the words as deeply as you can; **visualize how you'd feel if these words were true;** who are you, what are you doing, how are you expressing yourself if this was the truth?

Remember, healing and growth take time, and there **might be days when you doubt the effectiveness of affirmations.**

But **keep going.**

We **all have bad days.**

Be patient with yourself, embrace the process, and **celebrate even the smallest victories along the way.**

Practicing **as you wake up** and **just before you go to sleep** supercharges this practice as your subconscious mind is in a **deep meditative state and more open to suggestion.**

Try to **practice this for 30 days in a row, see how it makes you feel - you might be surprised.**

AFFIRMATIONS FOR BREAKING DISORGANIZED PATTERNS

Choose **3 of your favorite affirmations** and repeat them daily.

Reword them to feel more authentic to you.

Remember to **connect the words to an emotion,** so that your mind and body believe you.

1. I am worthy of love and belonging.
2. My feelings are valid and deserve to be acknowledged.
3. I have the power to create secure and fulfilling relationships.
4. I release the pain of my past and embrace the possibilities of my present.
5. I am open to giving and receiving love in a balanced way.
6. My needs are important, and I communicate them with clarity.
7. I choose to build bridges of connection, not walls of protection.
8. I am in control of my reactions, and I choose calmness and understanding.
9. Trusting others is a strength, and I'm growing stronger every day.
10. I am constantly learning, growing, and evolving in my relationships.
11. I am capable of creating the stability and safety I need.
12. I am more than my past experiences; I am resilient and adaptable.
13. I deserve relationships that are nurturing and empowering.
14. I am an anchor for myself; I find peace and security within.
15. My journey of healing is shaping me into a compassionate partner and friend.
16. My self-awareness is a tool for transformation.
17. I am an active participant in my relationships, not a passive observer.
18. My voice matters, and I share my thoughts and feelings with courage.
19. I am committed to setting healthy boundaries in my relationships.
20. The love I give is a reflection of the love I have for myself.
21. I am deserving of patience and understanding from myself and others.
22. I am not defined by my attachment style; I have the power to change.
23. Every day, I become more in tune with my emotions and needs.
24. I am building a future of secure attachments and mutual respect.
25. I acknowledge my growth, and I am proud of the steps I am taking towards healing.

A NEW YOU

A NEW YOU

So, do you think you can **cultivate a secure attachment style after everything you've learned?**

Secure attachment is characterized by **emotional responsiveness, trust, effective communication, and shared values.** By understanding the qualities that define secure attachment, you'll gain valuable insights to shape and enhance your own connections.

A secure attachment style comes with a certain flair for **maintaining healthy relationships.**

Here's what a person with a **secure attachment style** typically does:

1. **Communicates Openly:** They're adept at expressing their feelings and needs in a clear, respectful manner, fostering mutual understanding and reducing conflicts.
2. **Respects Boundaries:** They understand and respect personal boundaries, their own and those of others. They know that personal space and mutual respect go hand-in-hand in any relationship.
3. **Maintains Balance:** They find a healthy balance between dependence and independence, never too clingy, never too distant.
4. **Shows Empathy:** They can attune to the feelings and needs of their partners, offering support and understanding when needed.
5. **Cultivates Trust:** They trust easily but not naively, building trust with time and through consistent, reliable behavior.
6. **Is Resilient:** They bounce back from relationship setbacks, using them as opportunities to learn and grow rather than reasons to disconnect.
7. **Practices Self-Care:** They understand the importance of self-care and take time for themselves to recharge, knowing that a healthy relationship starts with a healthy self.

In essence, a secure attachment style is like **being in a dance where you're in sync with your partner**, flowing effortlessly together, yet also comfortable in your own rhythm.

We hope you feel this in your next meaningful relationship.

A NEW YOU

If you've gotten this far, wow, **you've done amazing!**

We hope that you've learnt some **cool things about neuroscience, your brain and how it's possible to change and grow.**

You've made it through a **pretty intense journey of introspection** and transformation, dealing with your disorganized attachment.

You may have **cried a little or came to a few realizations about yourself and life**; and we hope this has helped.

You've taken a **deep dive into your past, observed your present** through a new lens, and **envisioned an empowering future.**

By gaining insights into the patterns and behaviors associated with disorganized attachment, you have taken a **significant step towards healing and creating healthier relationships.**

As you move forward, **celebrate each milestone and progress you make** in building healthier and more secure attachments.

Don't ever forget - **you are capable, you are resilient, and you are deserving of love, connection,** and **joy in all its forms.**

Keep this journal close.

Revisit it often to **remind yourself of how far you've come** and the resilience you've displayed.

And as you move forward, **remember to be gentle with yourself.**

Healing is a **journey**, not a destination.

You got this.

Made in the USA
Coppell, TX
05 March 2025

46738858R00157

TRIGGER WARNING

This journal engages with deep and often challenging aspects of personal development, such as emotional trauma, attachment styles, personal insecurities, and the navigation of psychological complexities. It is designed to facilitate self-reflection and growth.

Please approach the exercises within with care. If any content brings up distressing emotions or overwhelming thoughts, prioritize your emotional safety and consider seeking the support of a qualified mental health professional. This journal is not a substitute for professional psychological services or medical advice.

Remember to move at a pace that feels right for you and to practice self-compassion throughout your journey.

HOW TO HEAL A DISORGANIZED ATTACHMENT STYLE

WORKBOOK